2018 SQA Specimen and Past Papers with Answers

National 5
BIOLOGY

2017 & 2018 Exams
and 2017 Specimen Question Paper

Hodder Gibson Study Skills Advice – National 5 Biology — page 3
Hodder Gibson Study Skills Advice – General — page 5
2017 EXAM — page 7
2017 SPECIMEN QUESTION PAPER — page 49
2018 EXAM — page 93
ANSWERS — page 137

HODDER
GIBSON
AN HACHETTE UK COMPANY

This book contains the official SQA 2017 and 2018 Exams, and the 2017 Specimen Question Paper for National 5 Biology, with associated SQA-approved answers modified from the official marking instructions that accompany the paper.

In addition the book contains study skills advice. This has been specially commissioned by Hodder Gibson, and has been written by experienced senior teachers and examiners in line with the new National 5 syllabus and assessment outlines. This is not SQA material but has been devised to provide further guidance for National 5 examinations.

Hodder Gibson is grateful to the copyright holders, as credited on the final page of the Answers section, for permission to use their material. Every effort has been made to trace the copyright holders and to obtain their permission for the use of copyright material. Hodder Gibson will be happy to receive information allowing us to rectify any error or omission in future editions.

Hachette UK's policy is to use papers that are natural, renewable and recyclable products and made from wood grown in sustainable forests. The logging and manufacturing processes are expected to conform to the environmental regulations of the country of origin.

Orders: please contact Bookpoint Ltd, 130 Park Drive, Milton Park, Abingdon, Oxon OX14 4SE. Telephone: (44) 01235 827827. Fax: (44) 01235 400454. Lines are open 9.00–5.00, Monday to Saturday, with a 24-hour message answering service. Visit our website at www.hoddereducation.co.uk. Hodder Gibson can also be contacted directly at hoddergibson@hodder.co.uk

This collection first published in 2018 by
Hodder Gibson, an imprint of Hodder Education,
An Hachette UK Company
211 St Vincent Street
Glasgow G2 5QY

Typeset by Aptara, Inc.

Printed in the UK

A catalogue record for this title is available from the British Library

ISBN: 978-1-5104-5596-2

2 1

2019 2018

Introduction

National 5 Biology

This book of SQA past papers contains the question papers used in the 2017 and 2018 exams (with answers at the back of the book). A specimen question paper reflecting the content and duration of the exam in 2018 is also included.

All of the question papers included in the book provide excellent representative exam practice for the final exams. Using these papers as part of your revision will help you to develop the vital skills and techniques needed for the exam and will help you identify any knowledge gaps you may have.

It is always a very good idea to refer to SQA's website for the most up-to-date course specification documents. These are available for each subject at www.sqa.org.uk/sqa/45723

The Course

The National 5 Biology course consists of three areas of biology. These are *Cell Biology*, *Multicellular Organisms* and *Life on Earth*. In each of the areas you will be assessed on your ability to demonstrate and apply knowledge of Biology, and to demonstrate and apply skills of scientific inquiry. Candidates complete an Assignment in which they investigate and research a topic in biology and write it up as a report. They also take a Course Examination.

How the Course is graded

The grade you get for National 5 Biology depends on the following two Course assessments, which are set and graded by SQA.

1   An **Assignment** in which candidates spend up to 8 hours investigating and researching a biological topic and producing a written report under exam conditions. The Assignment makes up 20% of your grade and is marked out of 20 marks, most of which are allocated for skills of scientific inquiry.

2   A written **Course Examination**, which is worth the remaining 80% of the grade. The Examination is marked out of 100 marks, most of which are for the demonstration and application of knowledge, although there are also marks available for skills of scientific inquiry. This book should help you practise the Examination part!

To pass National 5 Biology with a C grade you will need about 50% of the 120 marks available for the Assignment and the Course Examination combined. For a B, you will need 60%, and for an A, 70%.

The Course Examination

The Course Examination is a single question paper split into two sections. The first section is an objective test with 25 multiple choice items for 25 marks. The second section is a mixture of restricted and extended response questions worth between 1 and 4 marks each for a total of 75 marks. Some questions will contain options and there will usually be a question that asks you to suggest changes to experimental methods. Altogether there are 80 marks, and you will have two and a half hours to complete the paper. Most of the marks are for knowledge and its application, with the remainder of questions designed to test skills of scientific inquiry.

The majority of the marks will be straightforward – these are the marks that will help you get a grade C. Some questions will be more demanding – these are the questions you need to get right to get a grade A.

General hints and tips

You should have a copy of the Course Specification for National 5 Biology – if you haven't got one, download it from the SQA website mentioned earlier. This document tells you what you may be tested on in your examination. It is worth spending some time studying this document.

This book contains three question papers. The last two papers are a specimen paper (which was written to show exactly how the examination question paper would be constructed according to the new specification) and the official 2018 Past Paper. Both follow the new specification. The first paper is from 2017. Although this is very similar to the new examination question paper, it only has 80 marks overall. However, it still represents very good practice for your exam.

NB: There are a very small number of marks in the 2017 (Paper 2, Q14a/c, 3 marks) paper that will no longer be appropriate for the N5 specification as the learning outcomes they test have been deleted.

If you are trying a whole examination paper from this book, give yourself a maximum of two and a half hours to complete it. Make sure that you spend time using the Answer section to mark your own work – it is especially useful if you can get someone to help you with this. You could even grade your work on an A–D basis.

The following hints and tips are related to examination techniques as well as avoiding common mistakes.

Remember that if you hit problems with a question, you should ask your teacher for help.

Section 1

25 multiple choice items   25 marks

- Answer on the grid provided.
- Do not spend more than about **40 minutes** on this section.
- Some individual questions might take longer to answer than others – this is quite normal and make sure you use scrap paper if a calculation or any working is needed.
- Some questions can be answered instantly – again, this is normal.
- **Do not leave blanks** – complete the grid for each question as you work through.
- Try to answer each question in your head **without** looking at the options. If your answer is there – you are home and dry!
- If you are not certain, choose the answer that seemed most attractive on **first** reading the answer options.
- If you are guessing, try to eliminate options before making your guess. If you can eliminate three – you are left with the correct answer even if you do not recognise it!

Section 2

Restricted and extended response   75 marks

- Spend about **110 minutes** on this section.
- Answer on the question paper. Try to write neatly and keep your answers on the support lines if possible – the lines are designed to take the full answer!
- A clue to answer length is the mark allocation – most questions are restricted to 1 mark and the answer can be quite short. If there are 2–4 marks available, your answer will need to be extended and may well have two, three or even four parts.
- The parts of each question usually test a single Key Area or set of scientific inquiry skills but remember some questions are **designed** to cover more than one Key Area.
- The grade C-type questions usually start with "**State**", "**Identify**", "**Give**" or "**Name**" and often need only a word or two in response. They will usually be worth one mark each.

- Questions that begin with "**Explain**", "**Suggest**" or "**Describe**" are usually grade A types and are likely to have more than one part to the full answer. You will usually have to write a sentence or two and there may be two or even three marks available.
- Questions that begin with "**Calculate**" will need some numerical working and will have a space left for this. Although it is recommended that you show working, it is not necessary to do so to score the marks.
- Make sure you read questions through twice before trying to answer – there is often very important information within the question.
- Using abbreviations like DNA and ATP is fine, and the bases of DNA can be given as A, T, G and C.
- Don't worry that a few questions are in unfamiliar contexts – that's the idea! Just keep calm and read the questions carefully.
- If a question contains a choice, be sure to spend a minute or two making the best choice for you. You will probably need to circle your choice – make sure you do so.
- In experimental questions, you must be aware of what variables are, why controls are needed and how reliability might be improved. It is worth spending time on these ideas – they are essential and will come up year after year.
- Some candidates like to use a highlighter pen to help them focus on the essential points of longer questions – this is a great technique.
- Remember that a **conclusion** can be seen from data, whereas an **explanation** will usually require you to supply some background knowledge as well.
- If you are asked to write a conclusion from experimental data, remember to relate it to the aim of the experiment.
- Remember to "**use values from the graph**" when describing graphical information in words if you are asked to do so.
- Complete graphs and charts neatly and carefully using a ruler for the tops of bars, pie chart sections and to connect points on line graphs. Include zeros on your scale where appropriate and use the data table headings for the axes labels. For line graphs, join the plot points with straight lines using a ruler. For bar charts use a ruler for the tops on the bars and in pie charts use a ruler for the sections.

- Look out for graphs with two Y axes – these need extra special concentration and anyone can make a mistake!
- If you are given space for a calculation you will very likely need to use it! A calculator is essential.
- The main types of calculation tend to be **ratios**, **averages** and **percentages** – make sure you can do these common calculations.
- Answers to calculations will not usually have more than two decimal places.

- Do not leave blanks. Always have a go, using the language in the question if you can.

Good luck!

Remember that the rewards for passing National 5 Biology are well worth it! Your pass will help you get the future you want for yourself. In the exam, be confident in your own ability. If you're not sure how to answer a question, trust your instincts and just give it a go anyway. Keep calm and don't panic! GOOD LUCK!

Study Skills – what you need to know to pass exams!

General exam revision: 20 top tips

When preparing for exams, it is easy to feel unsure of where to start or how to revise. This guide to general exam revision provides a good starting place, and, as these are very general tips, they can be applied to all your exams.

1. Start revising in good time.

Don't leave revision until the last minute – this will make you panic and it will be difficult to learn. Make a revision timetable that counts down the weeks to go.

2. Work to a study plan.

Set up sessions of work spread through the weeks ahead. Make sure each session has a focus and a clear purpose. What will you study, when and why? Be realistic about what you can achieve in each session, and don't be afraid to adjust your plans as needed.

3. Make sure you know exactly when your exams are.

Get your exam dates from the SQA website and use the timetable builder tool to create your own exam schedule. You will also get a personalised timetable from your school, but this might not be until close to the exam period.

4. Make sure that you know the topics that make up each course.

Studying is easier if material is in manageable chunks – why not use the SQA topic headings or create your own from your class notes? Ask your teacher for help on this if you are not sure.

5. Break the chunks up into even smaller bits.

The small chunks should be easier to cope with. Remember that they fit together to make larger ideas. Even the process of chunking down will help!

6. Ask yourself these key questions for each course:

- Are all topics compulsory or are there choices?
- Which topics seem to come up time and time again?

- Which topics are your strongest and which are your weakest?

Use your answers to these questions to work out how much time you will need to spend revising each topic.

7. Make sure you know what to expect in the exam.

The subject-specific introduction to this book will help with this. Make sure you can answer these questions:

- How is the paper structured?
- How much time is there for each part of the exam?
- What types of question are involved? These will vary depending on the subject so read the subject-specific section carefully.

8. Past papers are a vital revision tool!

Use past papers to support your revision wherever possible. This book contains the answers and mark schemes too – refer to these carefully when checking your work. Using the mark scheme is useful; even if you don't manage to get all the marks available first time when you first practise, it helps you identify how to extend and develop your answers to get more marks next time – and of course, in the real exam.

9. Use study methods that work well for you.

People study and learn in different ways. Reading and looking at diagrams suits some students. Others prefer to listen and hear material – what about reading out loud or getting a friend or family member to do this for you? You could also record and play back material.

10. There are three tried and tested ways to make material stick in your long-term memory:

- Practising – e.g. rehearsal, repeating
- Organising – e.g. making drawings, lists, diagrams, tables, memory aids
- Elaborating – e.g. incorporating the material into a story or an imagined journey

11. Learn actively.

Most people prefer to learn actively – for example, making notes, highlighting, redrawing and redrafting, making up memory aids, or writing past paper answers. A good way to stay engaged and inspired is to mix and match these methods – find the combination that best suits you. This is likely to vary depending on the topic or subject.

12. Be an expert.

Be sure to have a few areas in which you feel you are an expert. This often works because at least some of them will come up, which can boost confidence.

13. Try some visual methods.

Use symbols, diagrams, charts, flashcards, post-it notes etc. Don't forget – the brain takes in chunked images more easily than loads of text.

14. Remember – practice makes perfect.

Work on difficult areas again and again. Look and read – then test yourself. You cannot do this too much.

15. Try past papers against the clock.

Practise writing answers in a set time. This is a good habit from the start but is especially important when you get closer to exam time.

16. Collaborate with friends.

Test each other and talk about the material – this can really help. Two brains are better than one! It is amazing how talking about a problem can help you solve it.

17. Know your weaknesses.

Ask your teacher for help to identify what you don't know. Try to do this as early as possible. If you are having trouble, it is probably with a difficult topic, so your teacher will already be aware of this – most students will find it tough.

18. Have your materials organised and ready.

Know what is needed for each exam:

- Do you need a calculator or a ruler?
- Should you have pencils as well as pens?
- Will you need water or paper tissues?

19. Make full use of school resources.

Find out what support is on offer:

- Are there study classes available?
- When is the library open?
- When is the best time to ask for extra help?
- Can you borrow textbooks, study guides, past papers, etc.?
- Is school open for Easter revision?

20. Keep fit and healthy!

Try to stick to a routine as much as possible, including with sleep. If you are tired, sluggish or dehydrated, it is difficult to see how concentration is even possible. Combine study with relaxation, drink plenty of water, eat sensibly, and get fresh air and exercise – all these things will help more than you could imagine. Good luck!

NATIONAL 5

2017

National Qualifications 2017

X707/75/02

**Biology
Section 1—Questions**

TUESDAY, 23 MAY
1:00 PM – 3:00 PM

Instructions for the completion of Section 1 are given on *Page two* of your question and answer booklet X707/75/01.

Record your answers on the answer grid on *Page three* of your question and answer booklet.

Before leaving the examination room you must give your question and answer booklet to the Invigilator; if you do not, you may lose all the marks for this paper.

SECTION 1

1. The following diagrams represent three different cells.

    P

    Q

    R

    Identify the plant cell(s).

    A   P and R only

    B   P and Q only

    C   P only

    D   R only

2. The graph shows the concentrations of ions in a single-celled organism and the sea water surrounding it.

    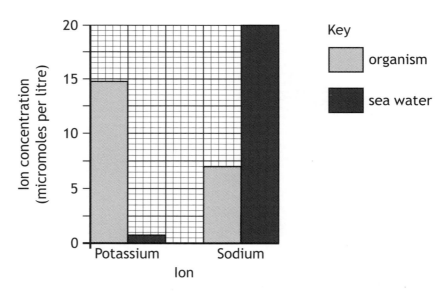

    Use the graph to identify which of the following statements is correct.

    A   Sodium ions will move into the organism by active transport.

    B   Sodium ions will move out of the organism by diffusion.

    C   Potassium ions will move out of the organism by active transport.

    D   Potassium ions will move into the organism by active transport.

3. Which row in the table identifies the order of stages involved in genetic engineering?

	Stage in Genetic Engineering			
	1st	2nd	3rd	4th
A	Required gene identified	Gene and plasmid extracted	Gene inserted into plasmid	Modified cells grown
B	Required gene identified	Gene inserted into plasmid	Gene and plasmid extracted	Modified cells grown
C	Gene inserted into plasmid	Required gene identified	Modified cells grown	Gene and plasmid extracted
D	Gene inserted into plasmid	Modified cells grown	Gene and plasmid extracted	Required gene identified

4. The graph shows the effect of increasing carbon dioxide concentration on the rate of photosynthesis.

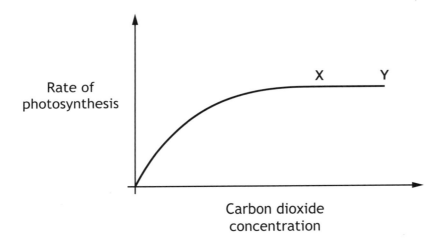

Two factors which could be limiting the rate of photosynthesis between points **X** and **Y** on the graph are

A   starch concentration and light intensity

B   temperature and light intensity

C   temperature and carbon dioxide concentration

D   sugar concentration and carbon dioxide concentration.

[Turn over

5. Which row in the table describes a process in plants which requires sugar and a substance into which sugar is converted?

	Process	Substance
A	Photosynthesis	Cellulose
B	Respiration	Starch
C	Photosynthesis	Protein
D	Respiration	ATP

6. What is the difference in the number of ATP molecules produced per glucose molecule by fermentation compared to aerobic respiration?

    A   2

    B   36

    C   38

    D   40

7. Which of the following shows terms listed in order of increasing level of organisation in a multicellular organism?

    A   organ ⟶ tissue ⟶ system

    B   organ ⟶ system ⟶ tissue

    C   tissue ⟶ system ⟶ organ

    D   tissue ⟶ organ ⟶ system

8. Stem cells are

    A   specialised cells which can divide to produce new stem cells

    B   specialised cells which are unable to divide to produce new stem cells

    C   non-specialised cells which can divide to produce new stem cells

    D   non-specialised cells which are unable to divide to produce new stem cells.

9. The diagram shows the main parts of a flower.

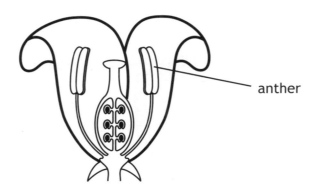

anther

Which row in the table describes the type of gametes produced by the anther and the chromosome complement these gametes contain?

	Type of gamete produced	Chromosome complement
A	female	diploid
B	male	diploid
C	female	haploid
D	male	haploid

10. Which of the following shows the passage of water through the tissues when it enters a plant?

A   root hair ⟶ xylem ⟶ spongy mesophyll

B   root hair ⟶ spongy mesophyll ⟶ xylem

C   spongy mesophyll ⟶ xylem ⟶ root hair

D   xylem ⟶ spongy mesophyll ⟶ root hair

[Turn over

11.   The diagram shows a villus from the small intestine.

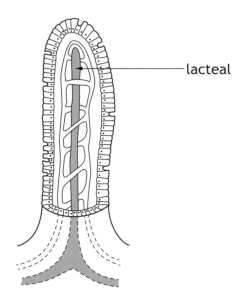

Which of the following products of digestion are both absorbed into the lacteal?

A   Glycerol and fatty acids

B   Glucose and fatty acids

C   Glycerol and amino acids

D   Glucose and amino acids

12.   The process which moves food along the digestive system is called

A   diffusion

B   absorption

C   peristalsis

D   osmosis.

13. Regular physical activity can help reduce the risk of heart disease.

The table shows the percentage of males and females of different age groups, who meet the weekly recommendations for physical activity.

Age group	Percentage meeting the weekly recommendations for physical activity	
	Males	Females
16–24	83	68
25–34	75	65
35–44	74	67
45–54	69	64
55–64	61	53

Which of the following statements is **not** correct for this data?

A   The percentage of males meeting the weekly recommendations always decreases as age increases.

B   The percentage of females meeting the weekly recommendations always decreases as age increases.

C   26% of males aged 35–44 do not meet the weekly recommendations.

D   35% of females aged 25–34 do not meet the weekly recommendations.

14. An example of a biotic factor affecting a population of plants is

A   a leaf disease reducing the growth of lettuce plants

B   acidic soil preventing the growth of daisies

C   shade from buildings causing a decrease in the growth of grass

D   a cold winter causing a decrease in the growth of geranium plants.

[Turn over

15. Which of the following statements is true of predation?

   A It is an abiotic factor and causes a decrease in prey numbers.

   B It is an abiotic factor and causes an increase in prey numbers.

   C It is a biotic factor and causes a decrease in prey numbers.

   D It is a biotic factor and causes an increase in prey numbers.

16. On average, 90% of energy is lost at each energy transfer in a food chain. Which of the following is a cause of this energy loss?

   A Digested material

   B Cell repair

   C Movement

   D Growth

17. The diagram below shows a pyramid of numbers.

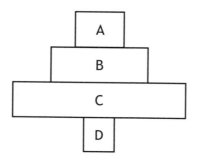

   Which letter represents the producer?

18. The following graph shows the changes in wheat yield over a fifty-year period.

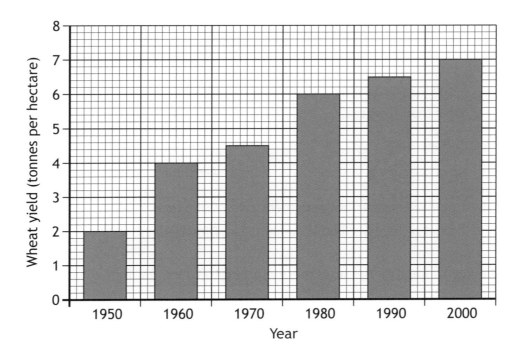

The percentage increase in wheat yield from 1950 to 2000 is

A   5

B   40

C   250

D   350.

19. Which row in the table describes a type of competition and a matching example?

	Type of competition	Example
A	Interspecific	Two birch trees growing close together in a wood
B	Interspecific	Lions and hyenas feeding on zebra
C	Intraspecific	Seals and dolphins feeding on small fish
D	Intraspecific	Buttercups and daisies growing in the same field

[Turn over

20. The following paired statement key can be used to identify invertebrate groups.

      1. Six legs .... *Hexapoda*
         More than six legs .... go to 2

      2. 8 legs .... go to 3
         More than 8 legs .... go to 4

      3. Curved sting .... *Dromopoda*
         No curved sting .... *Arachnida*

      4. 1 pair of legs per body segment....... *Chilopoda*
         2 pairs of legs per body segment...... *Diplopoda*

Use the key to identify the invertebrate group to which the following organism belongs.

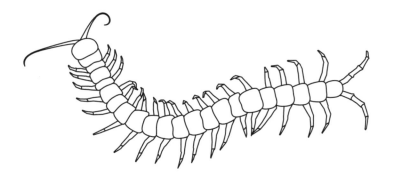

A   Dromopoda

B   Arachnida

C   Chilopoda

D   Diplopoda

**[END OF SECTION 1. NOW ATTEMPT THE QUESTIONS IN SECTION 2 OF
YOUR QUESTION AND ANSWER BOOKLET.]**

[BLANK PAGE]

DO NOT WRITE ON THIS PAGE

[BLANK PAGE]

DO NOT WRITE ON THIS PAGE

N5

National Qualifications 2017

Mark

X707/75/01

Biology
Section 1—Answer Grid and Section 2

TUESDAY, 23 MAY

1:00 PM — 3:00 PM

Fill in these boxes and read what is printed below.

Full name of centre

Town

Forename(s)

Surname

Number of seat

Date of birth

Day	Month	Year	Scottish candidate number

Total marks — 80

SECTION 1 — 20 marks

Attempt ALL questions.

Instructions for the completion of Section 1 are given on *Page two*.

SECTION 2 — 60 marks

Attempt ALL questions.

Write your answers clearly in the spaces provided in this booklet. Additional space for answers and rough work is provided at the end of this booklet. If you use this space you must clearly identify the question number you are attempting. Any rough work must be written in this booklet. You should score through your rough work when you have written your final copy.

Use **blue** or **black** ink.

Before leaving the examination room you must give this booklet to the Invigilator; if you do not, you may lose all the marks for this paper.

SECTION 1— 20 marks

The questions for Section 1 are contained in the question paper X707/75/02.

Read these and record your answers on the answer grid on *Page three* opposite.

Use **blue** or **black** ink. Do NOT use gel pens or pencil.

1. The answer to each question is **either** A, B, C or D. Decide what your answer is, then fill in the appropriate bubble (see sample question below).

2. There is **only one correct** answer to each question.

3. Any rough working should be done on the additional space for answers and rough work at the end of this booklet.

Sample Question

The thigh bone is called the

    A   humerus

    B   femur

    C   tibia

    D   fibula.

The correct answer is **B** — femur. The answer **B** bubble has been clearly filled in (see below).

Changing an answer

If you decide to change your answer, cancel your first answer by putting a cross through it (see below) and fill in the answer you want. The answer below has been changed to **D**.

If you then decide to change back to an answer you have already scored out, put a tick (✓) to the **right** of the answer you want, as shown below:

or

SECTION 1—Answer Grid

	A	B	C	D
1	○	○	○	○
2	○	○	○	○
3	○	○	○	○
4	○	○	○	○
5	○	○	○	○
6	○	○	○	○
7	○	○	○	○
8	○	○	○	○
9	○	○	○	○
10	○	○	○	○
11	○	○	○	○
12	○	○	○	○
13	○	○	○	○
14	○	○	○	○
15	○	○	○	○
16	○	○	○	○
17	○	○	○	○
18	○	○	○	○
19	○	○	○	○
20	○	○	○	○

[BLANK PAGE]

DO NOT WRITE ON THIS PAGE

MARKS | DO NOT WRITE IN THIS MARGIN

SECTION 2 — 60 marks
Attempt ALL questions

1. *Paramecium* is a single-celled organism which lives in fresh water.

   The following diagram shows some of its structures.

   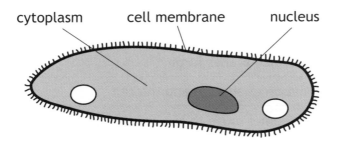

   cytoplasm　　cell membrane　　nucleus

   (a)　(i)　Choose one of the following structures by ticking (✓) one of the boxes and describe its function.　**1**

   Cytoplasm ☐　Cell membrane ☐　Nucleus ☐

   Function _____

   _____

   (ii)　The water concentration outside the paramecium is higher than the water concentration of the cytoplasm. This causes the diffusion of water into the cell.

   Name this movement of water.　**1**

   _____

   (b)　Name the structure present in a plant cell which prevents it from bursting when full of water.　**1**

   _____

   [Turn over

MARKS | DO NOT WRITE IN THIS MARGIN

2. (a) (i) The table describes some stages which occur during cell division, but not in the correct order.

The first stage has been given.

Identify the **third stage** by writing the number 3 beside its description.   1

Stage	Description
5	cytoplasm divides
4	nuclear membranes form
1	chromosomes shorten and thicken
2	chromosomes move to the equator of the cell
3	pairs of chromatids are pulled apart

(ii) The diagram represents a cell during one of the stages of mitosis.

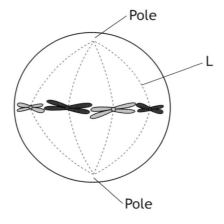

Name the part labelled L in the diagram.   1

_____

(b) During mitosis a pair of chromatids was pulled apart, each moving away from the equator, towards opposite poles, at a rate of 1 micrometre per second.

Calculate the distance between them after 20 seconds.   1

Space for calculation

_____micrometres

MARKS | DO NOT WRITE IN THIS MARGIN

3. (a) Forensic scientists can take small quantities of DNA and use a process to make large quantities. Each DNA molecule is separated and used to make two complementary strands as shown below.

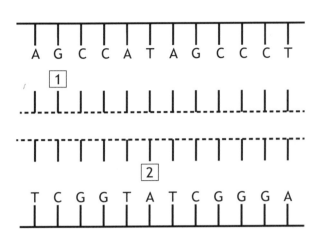

Key

Original strand of DNA

Complementary strand of DNA

Give the full names of bases labelled 1 and 2 in the diagram above.   2

1 _____

2 _____

(b) The bases in a strand of DNA make up the code for the production of proteins. The DNA for every individual person varies.

Describe the way in which this code differs from person to person.   1

_____

_____

(c) Name the single stranded molecule which carries a complementary copy of the code from the DNA in the nucleus to the ribosome for protein synthesis.   1

_____

[Turn over

MARKS | DO NOT WRITE IN THIS MARGIN

4. Catalase, an enzyme found in living tissues, is involved in the breakdown of hydrogen peroxide into water and oxygen.

   In an investigation, catalase was extracted in solution from a variety of tissues and used to soak paper discs. These discs were then dropped into beakers of hydrogen peroxide, as shown in Diagram 1. As the oxygen was released the discs returned to the surface, as shown in Diagram 2.

Diagram 1

Diagram 2

The time taken for these discs to return to the surface was recorded and shown in the table.

Type of tissue	Time for disc to return to the surface (s)
Apple	108
Banana	44
Carrot	68
Liver	8
Onion	70
Potato	72

MARKS | DO NOT WRITE IN THIS MARGIN

4. **(continued)**

(a) On the grid below, complete the vertical axis and the remaining bars to show the time taken for the discs to return to the surface, for each tissue.

2

(An additional grid, if required, can be found on *Page twenty-six*)

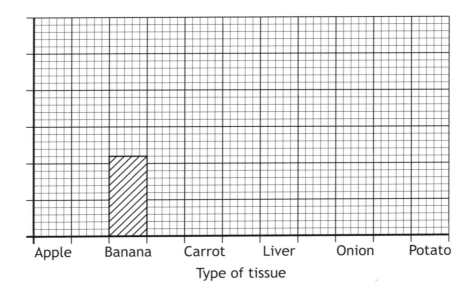

Type of tissue

(b) The aim of the experiment was to investigate catalase activity in a variety of tissues.

Using the information given, write an appropriate conclusion for this experiment.

1

Conclusion _____

_____

_____

(c) The experiment was carried out at pH 7, the optimum pH for catalase.

Complete the following sentence, using the words **increase, decrease** or **stay the same**, to predict what would happen if the experiment was repeated at pH 4.

1

At pH 4, the rate of oxygen production would_____

in each tissue.

[Turn over

MARKS | DO NOT WRITE IN THIS MARGIN

5. A student investigated the effect of temperature on the rate of respiration in germinating (growing) peas. Using the arrangement shown, four respirometers labelled A–D were set up at the temperatures shown in the table below.

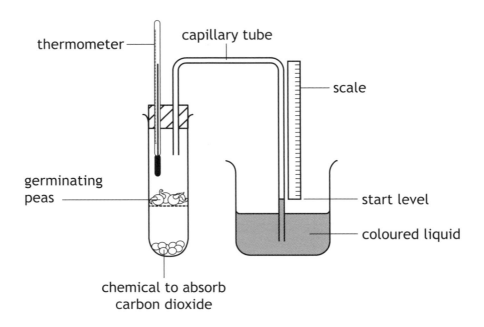

The level of the coloured liquid was measured on the scale at the start of the investigation and again after 20 minutes. The rise in liquid level was due to oxygen uptake by the germinating peas. The results are shown in the table.

Respirometer	Temperature (°C)	Contents	Rise in liquid level (mm)	Rate of oxygen uptake (mm per minute)
A	15	Germinating peas	14	0·7
B	15	Dead peas	0	0
C	25	Germinating peas	26	
D	25	Dead peas	0	0

(a) (i) Complete the table above by calculating the rate of oxygen uptake per minute by the peas in respirometer C.   1

Space for calculation

MARKS | DO NOT WRITE IN THIS MARGIN

5. (a) (continued)

(ii) Using the results from the table complete the following conclusion by <u>underlining</u> one option in the bracket.   1

Increasing the $\left\{ \begin{array}{l} \text{temperature} \\ \text{liquid level} \\ \text{oxygen uptake} \end{array} \right\}$ increases the rate of respiration in germinating peas.

(iii) Another respirometer was set up at 60°C with germinating peas and the coloured liquid did not rise. The student concluded that the peas were not respiring.

Explain why this temperature prevented the peas from carrying out respiration.   2

_____

_____

_____

(iv) Respirometers B and D were set up as control experiments.

Describe the purpose of the controls in **this** investigation.   1

_____

_____

_____

(b) The diagram below represents the fermentation pathway in a plant cell.

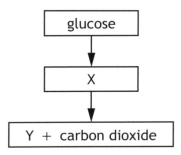

Choose either molecule X or Y and state its name.   1

Molecule _____

Name _____

MARKS | DO NOT WRITE IN THIS MARGIN

6. Chromosomes contain the genetic information responsible for variation amongst members of a species.

Fruit flies can have either a grey or black body colour.

The parent flies used in a cross are shown in the diagram.

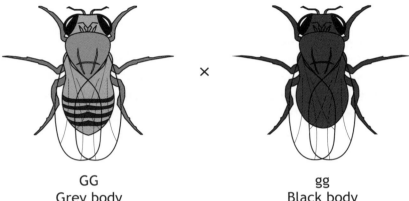

Genotype: GG   gg
Phenotype: Grey body   Black body

(a) Using the information given, <u>underline</u> one option in each bracket to complete the following sentences.

2

Body colour in fruit flies is an example of $\left\{\begin{array}{l}\text{discrete}\\\text{continuous}\end{array}\right\}$ variation.

The F_1 flies produced from this cross will be $\left\{\begin{array}{l}\text{homozygous}\\\text{heterozygous}\end{array}\right\}$.

MARKS | DO NOT WRITE IN THIS MARGIN

6.   (continued)

(b)   The diagram relates to sexual reproduction in humans.

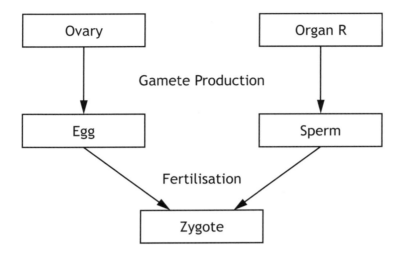

(i)   Name organ R.   1

_____

(ii)   Describe what happens during fertilisation.   1

_____

_____

_____

(iii)   An egg cell is haploid but a zygote is diploid.

Explain what this means in terms of the chromosome complement
found in each of these cells.   1

_____

_____

_____

_____

[Turn over

MARKS

7. (a) The table shows some information about causes of adult deaths in Scotland.

	Number of adult deaths (per 100 000 population)	
Cause of adult deaths	Males	Females
Cancer	385	274
Coronary heart disease	165	105
Chronic obstructive pulmonary disease	71	58

Calculate the simple whole number ratio of male deaths to female deaths due to coronary heart disease.

Space for calculation

1

_____ : _____

Males   Females

(b) (i) Coronary heart disease can gradually cause the coronary arteries to get narrower or become blocked completely.

Name **one** essential substance that will no longer be able to reach the cells in the heart if these arteries become blocked.

1

_____

(ii) A person has been told that they have a high risk of developing coronary heart disease.

Suggest a lifestyle choice that they could make, other than exercising more, to help reduce this risk.

1

_____

MARKS | DO NOT WRITE IN THIS MARGIN

7. **(continued)**

(c) Chronic obstructive pulmonary disease is a condition which affects the lungs. It can destroy the alveolar walls, leading to fewer alveoli.

The diagrams represent lung tissues which have undamaged and damaged alveoli.

undamaged   damaged

Identify a feature of the alveoli which will be affected by this reduction in their number.

1

_____

[Turn over

MARKS | DO NOT WRITE IN THIS MARGIN

8. A student investigated the link between transpiration rate and the number of leaf stomata.

A microscope was used to look at the number of stomata on a leaf surface of plant species A as shown.

Plant species A

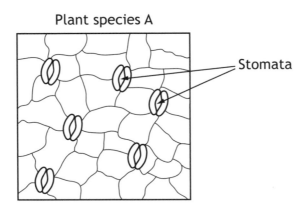

Stomata

The area shown on the diagram above measures 0·04 mm^2.

(a) Calculate the expected number of stomata present in 1 mm^2 on this leaf surface.

Space for calculation

1

_____

(b) A leaf from another plant, species B, had fewer stomata per mm^2 of leaf surface and a different rate of transpiration.

It was concluded that the number of stomata present affects the rate of transpiration.

(i) Suggest an advantage to plant species B of having fewer stomata.

1

_____

_____

(ii) Tick (✓) one box below to show the environmental condition to which this plant has become best adapted.

1

Dry ☐   Cool ☐   Moist ☐

MARKS | DO NOT WRITE IN THIS MARGIN

9. After a head injury, a student became dizzy and occasionally lost balance.

(a) Name the part of the brain which controls balance.   1

_____

(b) To test if there was also damage to the spinal cord, doctors touched different areas of the student's skin with a blunt needle.

Describe how the stimulus is detected at the skin and how the message is then carried into and across the spinal cord.   4

_____

_____

_____

_____

_____

_____

_____

_____

_____

_____

_____

_____

_____

[Turn over

MARKS | DO NOT WRITE IN THIS MARGIN

10. Type 1 diabetes occurs if the body does not produce any or enough insulin.

(a) (i) Name the organ which produces insulin.   1

_____

(ii) As a result of Type 1 diabetes, glucose is unable to enter the cells of the body. A symptom of this is extreme tiredness.

Using your knowledge of respiration, explain why a person suffering from diabetes might show extreme tiredness.   1

_____

_____

_____

(b) People with Type 1 diabetes need to inject insulin.

The table contains information about some of the different types of insulin available.

Type of insulin	Time for insulin to start working	Time for insulin levels to peak	Duration in blood (hours)
P	1 hour	No peak	20–26
Q	1–3 hours	8 hours	12–16
R	30–60 minutes	2–4 hours	5–8
S	15 minutes	30–90 minutes	3–5

Using information from the table, answer the following questions.

(i) A fast acting type of insulin can be injected just before meals.

Identify the type of insulin that is best suited for this.   1

_____

(ii) Another type of insulin can be injected once a day to provide a steady supply of insulin to the body.

Identify the type of insulin that would be most effective at doing this.   1

_____

MARKS | DO NOT WRITE IN THIS MARGIN

10. **(continued)**

(c) Diabetes also occurs if the target tissues in the body do not respond to insulin reaching them through the bloodstream.

Name the structures found on the surface of the target tissues that respond to the hormone insulin.

1

_____

[Turn over

MARKS | DO NOT WRITE IN THIS MARGIN

11. Certain varieties of potato plant are eaten by beetles, reducing the yield of potatoes. A beetle-resistant variety of potato plant was developed.

In an investigation, the beetle-resistant variety was grown outdoors in one field and the non-resistant variety grown in another.

The yields of both varieties were recorded and the results are shown in the graph below.

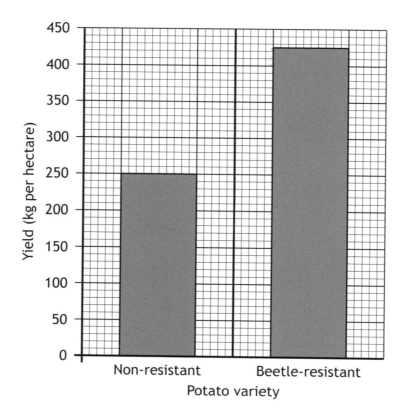

(a) Describe how the reliability of these results could be increased.　　1

_____

_____

(b) Calculate the difference in yield between the two varieties.　　1

Space for calculation

_____ kg per hectare

MARKS | DO NOT WRITE IN THIS MARGIN

11.   (continued)

(c)   Identify a variable that would have to be kept the same between the two fields to ensure the results were valid.

1

_____

(d)   Genetic engineering was used to develop the beetle-resistant variety of potato plant.

Before the development of genetic engineering, farmers used other methods to control the beetle numbers in their potato fields.

Name **one** of these methods.

1

_____

[Turn over

MARKS | DO NOT WRITE IN THIS MARGIN

12. The Scottish crossbill is a small bird which is native to Scotland. It inhabits pine forests in northern Scotland and feeds on pine seeds using its crossed beak.

(a) State the term used to describe the role of the Scottish crossbill within its community.   1

_____

(b) The shape of a crossbill's beak is a structural adaptation which is the result of a new allele being produced.

Name the process by which new alleles are produced.   1

_____

(c) The Scottish crossbill has been classified as a separate species, but can still mate with other species of crossbill.

Give a feature of any offspring produced from this mating, which proves that the parents are different species.   1

_____

MARKS | DO NOT WRITE IN THIS MARGIN

13. Decide if each of the following statements about evolution is **True** or **False** and tick (✓) the appropriate box.

If the statement is **False**, write the correct word in the **Correction** box to replace the word underlined in the statement.

3

Statement	True	False	Correction
Genetic variation within a population allows the population to <u>adapt</u> in a changing environment.			
Isolation barriers can be geographical, <u>environmental</u> or reproductive.			
Sub-populations evolve until they become genetically <u>identical</u>.			

[Turn over

MARKS | DO NOT WRITE IN THIS MARGIN

14. The flow of nitrogen in a fish farm is shown in the diagram below.

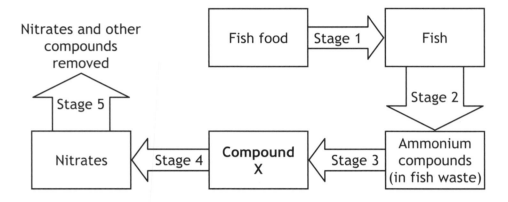

(a) (i) Name compound X.   1

_____

(ii) Give the number of a stage in the process shown above, which involves nitrifying bacteria.   1

Stage_____

(b) In the fish farm the nitrates have to be removed from the water to prevent build-up. In some situations living organisms remove nitrates from the soil.

(i) Name the type of organism which can absorb nitrates from the soil.   1

_____

(ii) Nitrates supply organisms with nitrogen.

State why nitrogen is required.   1

_____

(c) Decomposers, such as bacteria, help to break down waste and dead organisms.

Name another type of microorganism which carries out this role.   1

_____

MARKS | DO NOT WRITE IN THIS MARGIN

15. Levels of air pollution can be estimated by the presence or absence of organisms called lichens.

Air pollution level	Most common type of lichen present
Low	Shrubby
Medium	Leafy
High	Crusty

Environmental scientists carried out a study on lichen species at four different sites and obtained the results shown in the table below.

	Number of lichen species present		
Site	Shrubby	Leafy	Crusty
A	0	5	19
B	3	2	0
C	16	3	0
D	7	14	2

(a) (i) Site A had the highest levels of air pollution.

Using information from **both tables**, describe the evidence supporting this statement.   1

_____

_____

(ii) Calculate the average number of leafy lichen species present at the four sites.   1

Space for calculation

_____

(b) State the name given to species, such as lichen, which are used to estimate levels of pollution.   1

_____

[END OF QUESTION PAPER]

MARKS | DO NOT WRITE IN THIS MARGIN

ADDITIONAL SPACE FOR ANSWERS AND ROUGH WORK

ADDITIONAL GRID FOR QUESTION 4(a)

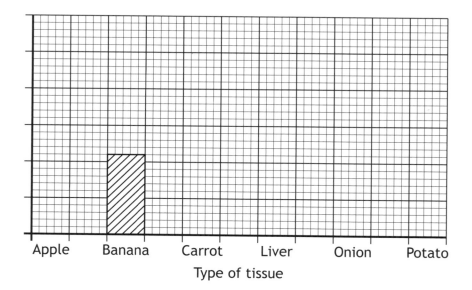

ADDITIONAL SPACE FOR ANSWERS AND ROUGH WORK

Page twenty-seven

MARKS | DO NOT WRITE IN THIS MARGIN

ADDITIONAL SPACE FOR ANSWERS AND ROUGH WORK

NATIONAL 5

2017 Specimen Question Paper

National
Qualifications
SPECIMEN ONLY

S807/75/02

**Biology
Section 1—Questions**

Date — Not applicable

Duration — 2 hours 30 minutes

Instructions for completion of Section 1 are given on *Page two* of your question and answer booklet S807/75/01.

Record your answers on the answer grid on *Page three* of your question and answer booklet.

Before leaving the examination room you must give your question and answer booklet to the Invigilator; if you do not, you may lose all the marks for this paper.

SECTION 1

1. The diagram shows a single cell.

    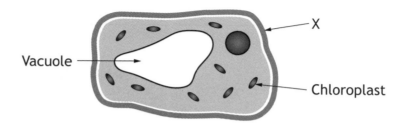

    The structure labelled X is made of

    A   starch

    B   cellulose

    C   protein

    D   phospholipid.

2. Plant cells were placed in a strong salt solution.

    Which of the following statements describes the state of the cells and the reason for this?

    A   Turgid due to water gain.

    B   Turgid due to water loss.

    C   Plasmolysed due to water gain.

    D   Plasmolysed due to water loss.

3. An enzyme reaction takes place because its active site is complementary to

    A   one type of substrate molecule

    B   all types of substrate molecule

    C   one type of product molecule

    D   all types of product molecules.

4. The diagram shows stages in the production of a substance by genetic engineering.

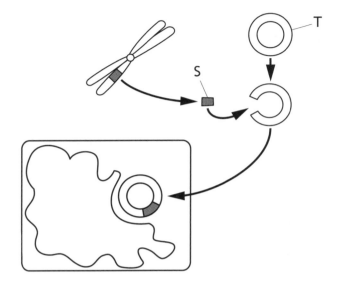

Which row in the table identifies S and T?

	S	T
A	Gene	Plasmid
B	Gene	Bacterium
C	Chromosome	Plasmid
D	Chromosome	Bacterium

5. In the United States of America, 95% of the sugar beet plants grown have been genetically modified (GM).

   The simple, whole number ratio of GM plants grown to non-GM plants is

   A   20:1

   B   1:20

   C   19:1

   D   1:19

6. Which of the following processes releases energy used to form ATP?

   A   Muscle cell contraction

   B   Breakdown of glucose

   C   Protein synthesis

   D   Nerve impulse transmission

7. Which of the following statements is **not** true of aerobic respiration?

    A   Produces carbon dioxide and water

    B   Begins in the cytoplasm

    C   Controlled by enzymes

    D   Requires light energy

8. An individual who possesses two different alleles for a particular gene would display a

    A   recessive phenotype

    B   recessive genotype

    C   dominant phenotype

    D   dominant genotype.

9. In humans the inheritance of wet or dry earwax is an example of discrete variation.

    The allele for wet earwax (E) is dominant to the allele for dry earwax (e).

    The diagram shows the inheritance of this characteristic.

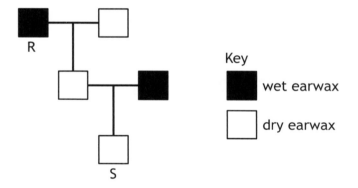

Key

■ wet earwax

□ dry earwax

    Which row in the table identifies the genotypes of individuals R and S?

	Genotype	
	Individual R	Individual S
A	EE	ee
B	Ee	ee
C	Ee	Ee
D	ee	EE

10. Which row in the grid gives correct information about stem cells?

A	Found in embryos	Specialised cells	Cannot self-renew
B	Found in tissues	Specialised cells	Can self-renew
C	Found in embryos	Unspecialised cells	Can self-renew
D	Found in tissues	Unspecialised cells	Cannot self-renew

11. The diagram shows some of the structures in a flower.

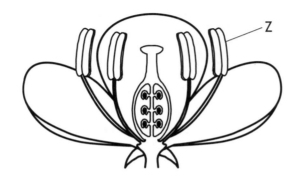

Which of the following is produced in the structure labelled Z?

A   Pollen

B   Anther

C   Ovule

D   Ovary

12. Which row in the table identifies the functions of phagocytes and lymphocytes?

	Phagocytes	Lymphocytes
A	produce antibodies	engulf pathogens
B	engulf pathogens	engulf pathogens
C	produce antibodies	produce antibodies
D	engulf pathogens	produce antibodies

[Turn over

13. The diagram shows some of the structures involved in transport in plants.

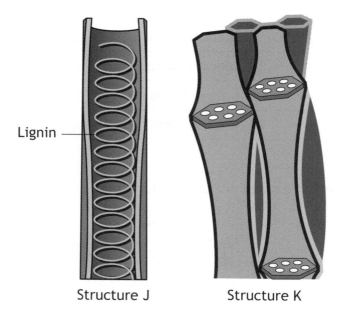

Lignin

Structure J   Structure K

Which row in the table identifies structures J and K, and the substances transported by them?

	Structure J		Structure K	
	Name	Substance transported	Name	Substance transported
A	Xylem	Water	Phloem	Sugar
B	Xylem	Sugar	Phloem	Water
C	Phloem	Water	Xylem	Sugar
D	Phloem	Sugar	Xylem	Water

Questions **14** and **15** refer to the diagram of the heart.

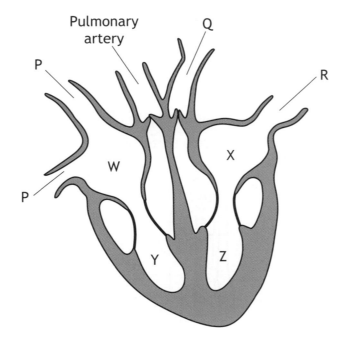

14. Which row in the table identifies the four chambers of the heart labelled W, X, Y and Z?

	W	X	Y	Z
A	Right ventricle	Left ventricle	Right atrium	Left atrium
B	Right ventricle	Left ventricle	Left atrium	Right atrium
C	Right atrium	Left atrium	Left ventricle	Right ventricle
D	Right atrium	Left atrium	Right ventricle	Left ventricle

15. Which row in the table identifies the type of blood carried in blood vessels P, Q and R?

	P	Q	R
A	deoxygenated	oxygenated	oxygenated
B	deoxygenated	oxygenated	deoxygenated
C	oxygenated	deoxygenated	oxygenated
D	oxygenated	deoxygenated	deoxygenated

16. Which of the following allows efficient gas exchange in the lungs?

A   Small number of thin walled alveoli

B   Large number of thin walled alveoli

C   Small number of thick walled alveoli

D   Large number of thick walled alveoli

17. The diagram shows a villus from the small intestine.

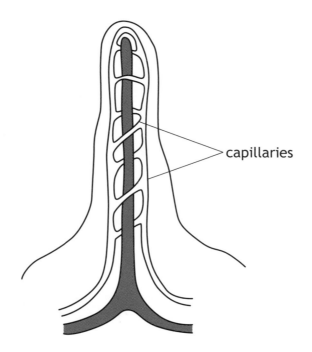

Which food molecules are absorbed into the capillaries of the villus?

A   Fatty acids and glycerol

B   Amino acids and gycerol

C   Amino acids and glucose

D   Fatty acids and glucose

18. Which row in the table identifies examples of biotic and abiotic factors?

	Biotic factor	*Abiotic factor*
A	Disease	Rainfall
B	Light intensity	Temperature
C	pH	Soil moisture
D	Predation	Food availability

19. Which of the following statements about a woodland describes a community?

A   All the oak trees.

B   All the plants.

C   All the oak trees and blackbirds.

D   All the plants and animals.

20. The diagram shows part of a food web in an oak woodland.

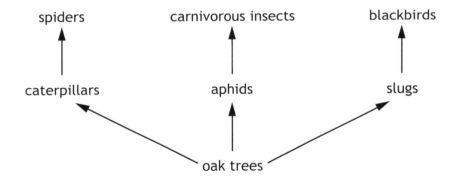

The use of pesticides in a nearby field resulted in the death of most aphids and caterpillars.

Which row in the table identifies the effect on the numbers of slugs and carnivorous insects?

	Number of slugs	*Number of carnivorous insects*
A	decreases	stays the same
B	increases	decreases
C	decreases	increases
D	increases	stays the same

Questions **21** and **22** refer to the following information.

An investigation was carried out into the effect of a hedge on the growth of wheat plants.

Groups of 100 wheat plants were planted at different distances from the hedge.

The heights of the wheat plants were measured after six weeks and the results are shown in the table.

Distance planted from hedge (m)	Average height of wheat plants after six weeks (cm)
2·0	45
2·5	54
3·0	60
3·5	69
4·0	78
4·5	90

21. The reliability of the results was increased by

   A   measuring the height of wheat plants after six weeks

   B   planting groups of 100 wheat plants

   C   planting the wheat plants at different distances from the hedge

   D   calculating an average height of wheat plants.

22. What is the percentage increase in average height of wheat planted between 2·0 m and 4·5 m from the hedge?

   A   45%

   B   50%

   C   66%

   D   100%

23. Which of the following graphs shows the effects of competition for the same food between a successful species and an unsuccessful species?

A

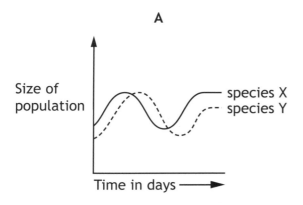

B

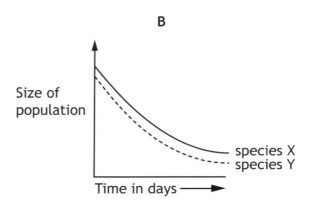

C

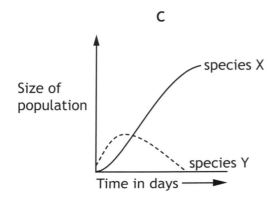

D

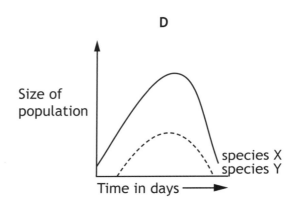

24. Survival of the fittest is also known as

    A   selection pressure

    B   natural selection

    C   selective advantage

    D   species selection.

[Turn over

25.   The diagram represents a population of animals.

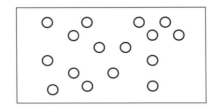

The following diagrams show the stages of speciation occurring from this population.

Stage

W

X

Y

Z

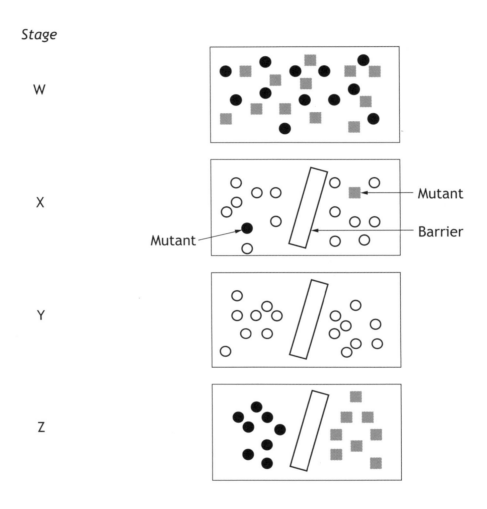

The correct order of the stages of speciation is

A   Z, W, X, Y

B   Z, X, W, Y

C   Y, X, Z, W

D   Y, Z, X, W.

[END OF SECTION 1. NOW ATTEMPT THE QUESTIONS IN SECTION 2
OF YOUR QUESTION AND ANSWER BOOKLET]

N5

National Qualifications
SPECIMEN ONLY

Mark

S807/75/01

Biology
Section 1—Answer Grid and Section 2

Date — Not applicable

Duration — 2 hours 30 minutes

Fill in these boxes and read what is printed below.

Full name of centre

Town

Forename(s)

Surname

Number of seat

Date of birth

Day	Month	Year

Scottish candidate number

Total marks — 100

SECTION 1 — 25 marks

Attempt ALL questions.

Instructions for completion of Section 1 are given on *Page two*.

SECTION 2 — 75 marks

Attempt ALL questions.

Write your answers clearly in the spaces provided in this booklet. Additional space for answers and rough work is provided at the end of this booklet. If you use this space you must clearly identify the question number you are attempting. Any rough work must be written in this booklet. Score through your rough work when you have written your final copy.

Use **blue** or **black** ink.

Before leaving the examination room you must give this booklet to the Invigilator; if you do not, you may lose all the marks for this paper.

SECTION 1 — 25 marks

The questions for Section 1 are contained in the question paper S807/75/02.

Read these and record your answers on the answer grid on *Page three* opposite.

Use **blue** or **black** ink. Do NOT use gel pens or pencil.

1. The answer to each question is **either** A, B, C or D. Decide what your answer is, then fill in the appropriate bubble (see sample question below).

2. There is **only one correct** answer to each question.

3. Any rough working should be done on the additional space for answers and rough work at the end of this booklet.

Sample Question

The thigh bone is called the

    A   humerus

    B   femur

    C   tibia

    D   fibula.

The correct answer is **B** — femur. The answer **B** bubble has been clearly filled in (see below).

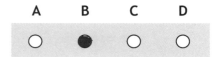

Changing an answer

If you decide to change your answer, cancel your first answer by putting a cross through it (see below) and fill in the answer you want. The answer below has been changed to **D**.

If you then decide to change back to an answer you have already scored out, put a tick (✓) to the **right** of the answer you want, as shown below:

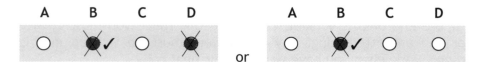

SECTION 1 — Answer Grid

	A	B	C	D
1	○	○	○	○
2	○	○	○	○
3	○	○	○	○
4	○	○	○	○
5	○	○	○	○
6	○	○	○	○
7	○	○	○	○
8	○	○	○	○
9	○	○	○	○
10	○	○	○	○
11	○	○	○	○
12	○	○	○	○
13	○	○	○	○
14	○	○	○	○
15	○	○	○	○
16	○	○	○	○
17	○	○	○	○
18	○	○	○	○
19	○	○	○	○
20	○	○	○	○
21	○	○	○	○
22	○	○	○	○
23	○	○	○	○
24	○	○	○	○
25	○	○	○	○

[BLANK PAGE]

DO NOT WRITE ON THIS PAGE

MARKS | DO NOT WRITE IN THIS MARGIN

SECTION 2 — 75 marks

Attempt ALL questions

1. A variegated leaf contains green areas and white areas.

    A student investigated cells from both areas.

    One of these cells is shown.

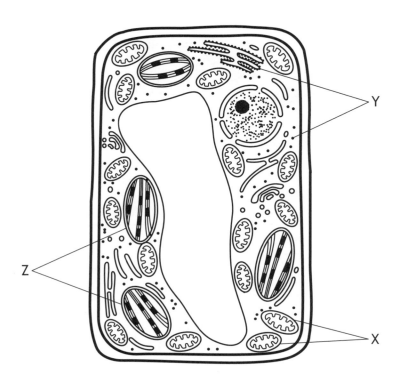

(a) Which letter identifies ribosomes?   1

     _____

(b) Give the evidence from the diagram which suggests that this cell
     produces large quantities of ATP.   1

     _____

(c) The student concluded that this cell is from the green area. Explain why
     this conclusion is correct.   2

     _____

     _____

[Turn over

MARKS | DO NOT WRITE IN THIS MARGIN

2. The diagram shows a site of gas exchange in the lungs.

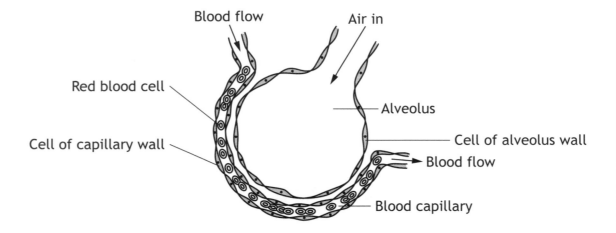

The table shows the relative concentration of oxygen, carbon dioxide and water in three cell types.

Cell Type	Relative concentration of substances		
	Oxygen	Carbon dioxide	Water
Red blood cell	low	high	medium
Cell of capillary wall	medium	medium	medium
Cell of alveolus wall	high	low	medium

(a) (i) Describe the pathway that oxygen would take when moving between these cell types.   1

_____

_____

(ii) Explain why oxygen moves along this pathway.   1

_____

_____

(b) Osmosis would not occur between the cells of the capillary wall and the cells of the alveolus wall.   1

Using the information provided, explain why this is the case.

_____

_____

MARKS | DO NOT WRITE IN THIS MARGIN

3. The diagram shows how genetic information in the nucleus is used in the first stage of making a protein.

inside the nucleus

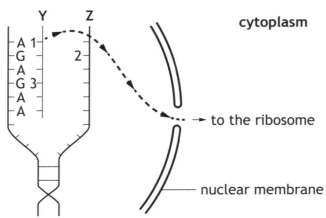

(a) (i) Name molecule **Y**.   1

_____

(ii) Underline one option in each bracket to complete the following sentences.   2

The molecules represented by the letter **A** are ⎰ bases / amino acids / proteins. ⎱

The complementary strand **Z** would have the letter ⎰ A / C / G / T ⎱ at position **2** in the diagram.

(b) State the name given to a section of DNA which codes for a protein.   1

_____

(c) The diagram above shows a section of the code to make a protein such as the enzyme amylase.

Describe how the code to make the protein insulin would differ from this.   1

_____

_____

MARKS | DO NOT WRITE IN THIS MARGIN

4. A study was carried out into the percentage of amino acids present in the blood of people with different diets.

One group tested were meat eaters and the other group were vegetarians.

In both groups, samples were analysed to show the percentage of amino acids in their food and in their blood after digesting the food.

The results are shown in the table.

Amino acid	Amino acid present (%)			
	Meat eaters		Vegetarians	
	In food	In blood	In food	In blood
Arginine	5·5	1·6	6·4	1·4
Leucine	8·0	5·4	7·0	5·0
Lysine	6·4	6·4	4·8	4·8
Serine	4·8	5·4	5·0	5·4
Threonine	4·0	3·8	3·8	3·8
Tyrosine	3·2	2·0	3·0	1·8

(a) Select the amino acid which

   (i) is least well absorbed into the blood in both groups;   1

   _____

   (ii) is completely absorbed from food into blood in both groups;   1

   _____

   (iii) must be obtained from other sources as well as from food.   1

   _____

(b) Calculate the simple, whole number ratio for tyrosine to serine in the blood of vegetarians.   1

Space for calculation

_____   :   _____

        tyrosine   serine

4. **(continued)**

(c) On the grid below, add a scale and complete the remaining 5 bars to show the percentage of amino acids in the **blood of both groups.**   2

(An additional grid, if required, can be found on *Page twenty-nine*)

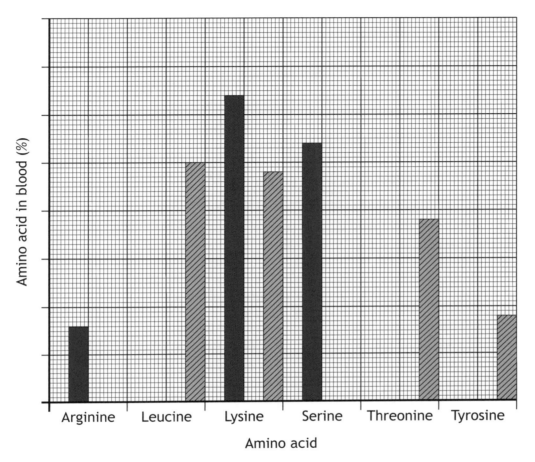

Key Meat eaters - Amino acid in blood

Vegetarians - Amino acid in blood

[Turn over

MARKS | DO NOT WRITE IN THIS MARGIN

5. An investigation was carried out to find the effect of pH on fermentation by yeast, using the apparatus shown.

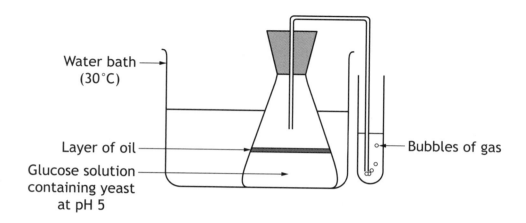

Water bath (30°C)

Layer of oil

Glucose solution containing yeast at pH 5

Bubbles of gas

The investigation was repeated at pH 3, pH 7 and pH 9.

The number of bubbles produced per minute was counted.

Six groups carried out the investigation several times and calculated average values for their results, as shown in the table.

Group	Average number of bubbles produced per minute			
	pH 3	pH 5	pH 7	pH 9
1	8	25	17	0
2	10	21	13	3
3	15	23	14	0
4	17	22	16	0
5	19	24	12	1
6	22	17	18	9

(a) Name the gas produced during fermentation in yeast. 1

_____

(b) From the table, identify the optimum pH for fermentation by yeast and give a reason for your choice.

pH _____ 1

Reason _____ 1

MARKS | DO NOT WRITE IN THIS MARGIN

5. (continued)

(c) This investigation could be adapted to find the effect of a variable other than pH.

Choose **one** variable from the list.

Describe **two** ways that the apparatus would be adapted to demonstrate the effect of this variable.   **2**

List

Type of yeast

Temperature

Concentration of glucose solution

Variable _____

Adaptation 1 _____

_____

Adaptation 2 _____

_____

[Turn over

MARKS | DO NOT WRITE IN THIS MARGIN

6. The diagrams show a cell in different stages of mitosis.

(a) Use letters from the diagrams to complete the correct order of the stages.   1

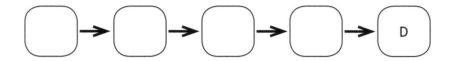

(b) Describe what is happening in stage C.   1

_____

_____

(c) Explain why it is important for the new cells produced to be identical to the original cell.   1

_____

_____

(d) Calculate the number of times the original cell would have to divide to form 128 cells in total.   1

Space for calculation

_____ times

MARKS | DO NOT WRITE IN THIS MARGIN

7. (a) The diagram shows a hormone, such as insulin, binding with its target cell.

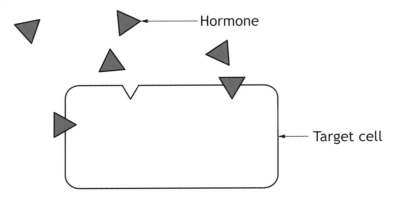

Hormone

Target cell

(i) Explain why a hormone only works on its target cell.　1

_____

_____

(ii) Hormone messages travel more slowly than nerve messages.
State one other difference between these messages.　1

_____

_____

[Turn over

7. **(continued)**

(b) Diabetes is a condition in which the blood glucose level is not fully controlled by insulin. There are two types of diabetes. The table shows information about both types.

Type 1 diabetes	Type 2 diabetes
Insulin is not produced	Insulin is produced but is not used effectively
Often starts at a young age	Often associated with being obese
Can be triggered by infection	Can be controlled with diet and exercise
Treated with daily insulin injections	Medication can be given in tablet form

A person with diabetes was treated with daily insulin injections.

(i) Using information from the table, state which type of diabetes this person had and why this treatment was required.

1

(ii) Describe what would happen to this person's blood glucose level if they had not been treated.

1

(iii) Name the organ which, if not functioning properly, results in type 1 diabetes.

1

MARKS | DO NOT WRITE IN THIS MARGIN

8. Hair type in humans is genetically controlled.

The dominant form is curly hair (H). The recessive form (h) produces straight hair.

Both parents of this curly-haired child have the genotype Hh.

(a) State the term used to describe the genotype of both parents. 1

_____

(b) Complete the Punnett square to show the possible genotypes of their offspring. 1

Male gametes

		H	h
	H		
Female gametes	**h**		

(c) Give the possible genotypes of the girl in the picture. 1

_____

[Turn over

Page fifteen

MARKS | DO NOT WRITE IN THIS MARGIN

9. An experiment was set up as shown to measure the transpiration rate of a plant at room temperature. The mass was recorded at the start and again after 6 hours. The results are shown in the table.

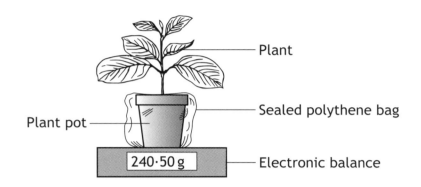

Mass at start (g)	Mass after 6 hours (g)
240·50	232·04

It was assumed that the loss in mass was due to the evaporation of water.

(a) Explain why it was necessary to cover the plant pot with a polythene bag.   1

_____

_____

(b) Calculate the average loss in mass from this plant per hour.   1

Space for calculation

_____ g per hour

(c) Describe a suitable control for this experiment.   1

_____

_____

(d) Predict the effect on the mass lost by the plant if the temperature of the room had been decreased.   1

_____

(e) Name the openings through which the water evaporated from the leaves of the plant.   1

_____

MARKS | DO NOT WRITE IN THIS MARGIN

10. (a) Blood travels in three types of blood vessels.

Compare the structure of **two** of these types of vessels.   3

_____

_____

_____

_____

_____

_____

_____

_____

_____

_____

_____

_____

(b) State the function of haemoglobin found in red blood cells.   1

_____

[Turn over

MARKS | DO NOT WRITE IN THIS MARGIN

11. (a) Cichlid fish are all found in Lake Malawi in Africa.

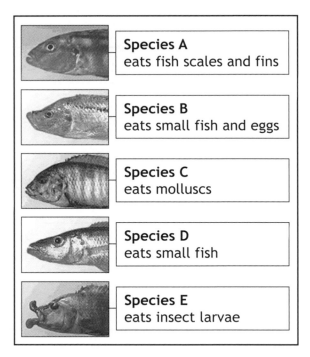

Species A
eats fish scales and fins

Species B
eats small fish and eggs

Species C
eats molluscs

Species D
eats small fish

Species E
eats insect larvae

(i) Using the information shown, identify the feature which enables Cichlid fish to have different diets. **1**

_____

(ii) Predict **two** species of Cichlid which would be in competition with each other if there was a shortage of fish eggs. **1**

Species _____ and _____

(b) State the term which describes the role that an organism, such as the Cichlid fish, plays within its community. **1**

_____

MARKS | DO NOT WRITE IN THIS MARGIN

11. (continued)

(c) Fresh water environments, such as Lake Malawi, can be affected by the overuse of fertilisers. This can impact on the organisms living in these environments.

The following statements show how this might occur, but not in the correct order.

1. Chemicals leach into water

2. Fish die

3. Overuse of fertilisers

4. Oxygen levels decrease

5. Algal bloom develops

Place a statement number in each box to complete the sequence of events.   **1**

(d) A fresh water environment is an example of an ecosystem.

Describe what is meant by the term ecosystem.   **1**

_____

_____

[Turn over

MARKS | DO NOT WRITE IN THIS MARGIN

12. (a) Photosynthesis is the process by which plants produce sugar using light.

The flow diagram represents some stages of photosynthesis in a leaf.

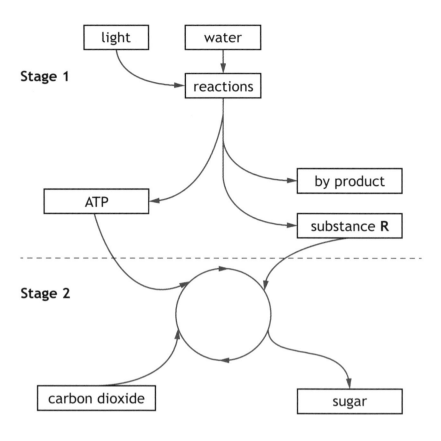

(i) Identify substance R.   1

_____

(ii) Describe the transfer of energy in stage 1 from light arriving at the leaf, and how the sugar produced in stage 2 can be used by the plant.   3

_____

_____

_____

_____

_____

_____

_____

_____

MARKS | DO NOT WRITE IN THIS MARGIN

12.   (continued)

(b) The graph shows the effect of light intensity and carbon dioxide concentration on the rate of photosynthesis.

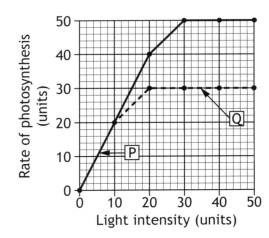

Identify the limiting factor at each of the points P and Q.   **2**

P _____

Q _____

[Turn over

MARKS DO NOT WRITE IN THIS MARGIN

Adapted from, Herald, Saturday 19th September 2015

13. **Beetroot juice**

Scientists have a theory that drinking nitrate-rich beetroot juice has an effect on both sprint performance and decision making during sports.

In a study, 16 male rugby and football players drank 140ml of a nitrate-rich beetroot juice every day for seven days.

The players then completed a sprint test on an exercise bike. This consisted of repeated sessions of two minute blocks - a 10 second sprint, 80 seconds of slow pedalling and 30 seconds of rest. At the same time, they were given thinking tasks designed to test how accurately and quickly they made decisions.

The players completed these tests again after drinking 140ml of the same juice, with the nitrate removed, every day for another seven days.

When they had taken the nitrate-rich juice, the players saw a 3·5% improvement in sprint performance and a 3% increase in their speed of their decision making.

The improvement may seem small, but it could mean the players are able to make important decisions faster and cover more ground than their opponents in the seconds when it matters most.

(a) Suggest the aim of the research described in the passage.   1

_____

_____

(b) A dependent variable is what scientists measure or observe as a result of the changes they make in their investigation.

Identify the dependent variable in this investigation.   1

_____

MARKS | DO NOT WRITE IN THIS MARGIN

13. **(continued)**

(c) Complete the table, with suitable headings, to show the activities and timings of the two minute sprint test.   2

(An additional table, if required, can be found on *Page twenty-nine*)

(d) What conclusion did the scientists draw from this study?   1

_____

_____

(e) Give a reason why it could be suggested that the results of the investigation might be unreliable.   1

_____

_____

[Turn over

MARKS | DO NOT WRITE IN THIS MARGIN

14. (a) A food chain is shown along with three pyramids of numbers.

grass ⟶ zebra ⟶ lion ⟶ flea

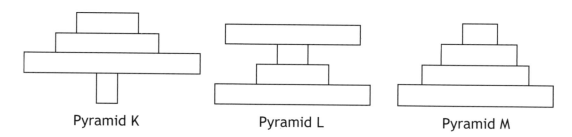

Pyramid K   Pyramid L   Pyramid M

Identify the pyramid which represents the food chain shown.   1

Pyramid _____

(b) This food chain can also be represented by a pyramid of energy.
State the meaning of the term pyramid of energy.   1

_____

_____

(c) State one way in which energy may be lost between stages in a food chain.   1

_____

[Turn over

MARKS | DO NOT WRITE IN THIS MARGIN

15. The number of farmland birds in Europe has decreased dramatically in recent years. A study estimated that the total bird population has dropped from 600 million to 300 million between 1980 and 2009.

It has been suggested that the use of pesticides may have killed many of the insects that are eaten by bird species.

The effect on the populations of some bird species is shown in the table.

Bird species	Population in 1980 (millions)	Population in 2009 (millions)	Population decrease (%)
Linnet	37·0	14·0	62
Meadow pipit	34·9	12·9	63
Corn bunting	27·2	9·2	66
Starling	84·9	39·9	53
Whinchat	10·4	3·4	67
Yellow wagtail	9·4	4·4	53

(a) Explain why the population decrease was expressed as a percentage rather than a decrease in number.   **1**

_____

_____

(b) Using information from **the passage and the table**, calculate the percentage of Meadow pipit in the total bird population in 2009.   **1**

Space for calculation

_____ %

(c) Identify the two species of birds which were least affected between 1980 and 2009.   **1**

_____ and _____

16. A group of students wanted to investigate the effect of various factors on the distribution of the plant Yellow Iris.

They set up a line transect and marked out five evenly spaced sample sites. The abundance of Yellow Iris was recorded, and values for soil temperature, pH and moisture were measured at the same sample sites.

MARKS | DO NOT WRITE IN THIS MARGIN

16. **(continued)**

The results are shown in the table.

Sample site	Soil temperature (°C)	Soil moisture (% saturation)	Soil pH	Yellow Iris abundance
1	12	15	5·4	0
2	13	39	5·5	3
3	11	56	5·6	9
4	12	78	5·5	21
5	11	90	5·4	25

(a) Describe the distribution of Yellow Iris along the transect line from sample site 1 to 5.

1

_____

(b) Identify which abiotic factor had the greatest effect on the distribution of Yellow Iris.

1

_____

(c) Probes were used to measure the soil moisture and soil pH.

Describe a precaution that should be taken when using a probe to make sure that the measurements are valid.

1

_____

_____

[Turn over for next question

MARKS | DO NOT WRITE IN THIS MARGIN

17. The table shows some features of common seaweeds.

Seaweed	Colour	Shape	Bladders
Bladder wrack	brown	branched	present in pairs
Cladophora	green	long and thin	absent
Spiral wrack	brown	twisted	present in pairs
Channel wrack	brown	grooved edges	absent
Egg wrack	brown	branched	present along its length
Sea lettuce	green	flat	absent
Serrated wrack	brown	saw-toothed edge	absent

(a) Use the information in the table to complete the key.   3

1. Green seaweed   go to 2
   Brown seaweed   go to 3

2. Flat   Sea lettuce
   [   ]   Cladophora

3. Bladders present   go to 4
   Bladders absent   go to 6

4. Bladders along its length   [   ]
   Bladders in pairs   go to 5

5. Twisted   Spiral wrack
   Branched   [   ]

6. Grooved edge   Channel wrack
   Saw-toothed edge   Serrated wrack

(b) Describe the difference that would allow a person to identify a piece of seaweed as Egg wrack or Bladder wrack.   1

_____

_____

(c) Identify a feature which Cladophora and Serrated wrack have in common.   1

_____

_____

[END OF SPECIMEN QUESTION PAPER]

ADDITIONAL SPACE FOR ANSWERS

Additional grid for Question 4 (c)

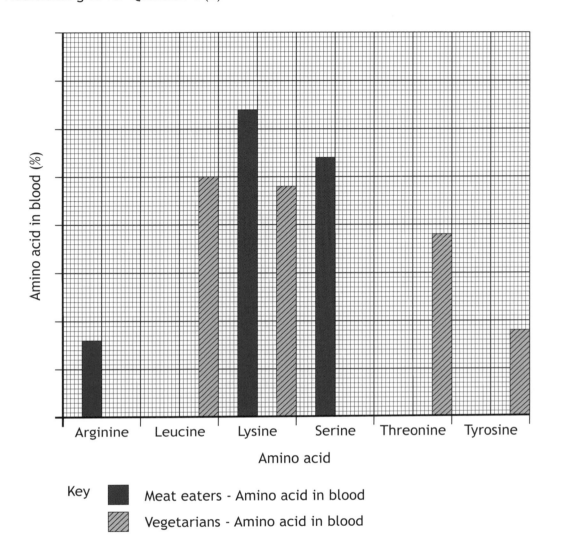

Key

Meat eaters - Amino acid in blood

Vegetarians - Amino acid in blood

Additional table for Question 13 (c)

MARKS | DO NOT WRITE IN THIS MARGIN

ADDITIONAL SPACE FOR ANSWERS

NATIONAL 5

2018

National Qualifications 2018

X807/75/02

Biology
Section 1—Questions

TUESDAY, 15 MAY

1:00 PM – 3:30 PM

Instructions for the completion of Section 1 are given on *Page two* of your question and answer booklet X807/75/01.

Record your answers on the answer grid on *Page three* of your question and answer booklet.

Before leaving the examination room you must give your question and answer booklet to the Invigilator; if you do not, you may lose all the marks for this paper.

SECTION 1

1. The diagram shows a cell with a section of the cell membrane magnified.

Magnified section

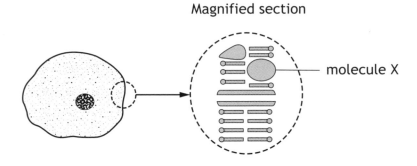

molecule X

Molecule X is

A   phospholipid

B   protein

C   cellulose

D   starch.

2. The diagram shows an experiment in which a model cell was placed in a sucrose solution.

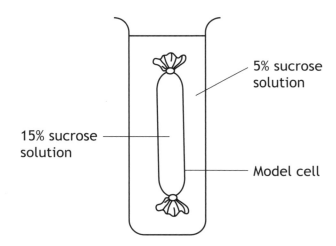

5% sucrose solution

15% sucrose solution

Model cell

At the start of the experiment the model cell weighed 25 g and at the end it weighed 30 g. What was the percentage increase in mass?

A   5·0%

B   16·7%

C   20·0%

D   83·3%

3. Glucose molecules in low concentration in the kidney have to be moved into the bloodstream, where there is a higher concentration of glucose.

   The process responsible for this action is

   A   osmosis

   B   diffusion

   C   passive transport

   D   active transport.

4. Which of the following represents the sequence of events in the production of a protein from the genetic code?

   A   DNA $\longrightarrow$ amino acids $\longrightarrow$ mRNA $\longrightarrow$ protein

   B   DNA $\longrightarrow$ mRNA $\longrightarrow$ amino acids $\longrightarrow$ protein

   C   mRNA $\longrightarrow$ DNA $\longrightarrow$ amino acids $\longrightarrow$ protein

   D   amino acids $\longrightarrow$ DNA $\longrightarrow$ mRNA $\longrightarrow$ protein

5. Which of the following are all types of proteins?

   A   Hormones, enzymes and nitrates

   B   Antibodies, enzymes and plasmids

   C   Hormones, receptors and antibodies

   D   Receptors, antibodies and nitrates

[Turn over

6. The flowchart represents some of the stages of genetic engineering.

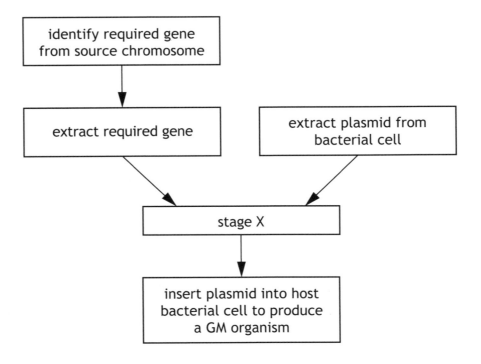

A suitable description of stage X would be

A   insert bacterial plasmid into required gene

B   insert bacterial plasmid into source chromosome

C   insert required gene into host bacterial cell

D   insert required gene into bacterial plasmid.

7. The diagram shows an experiment which can be used to find the energy content of different foods. Each food was completely burned and the energy content was estimated by the rise in temperature of the water.

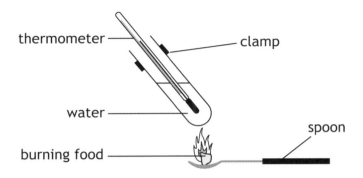

The reliability of this experiment could be improved by

A   burning each food for the same length of time

B   repeating the experiment with each food several times

C   removing the thermometer from the tube to read it accurately

D   repeating the experiment using a different food each time.

8. The apparatus shown was used to investigate the rate of respiration in yeast at 20 °C.

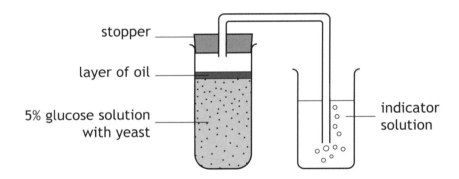

Which of the following changes would cause a decrease in the rate of respiration of the yeast?

A   Increase the thickness of the layer of oil by 1 mm.

B   Increase the temperature of the glucose solution by 1 °C.

C   Decrease the concentration of the glucose solution by 1%.

D   Decrease the volume of indicator solution by 1 cm³.

[Turn over

9. The diagram shows some of the structures found in a reflex arc.

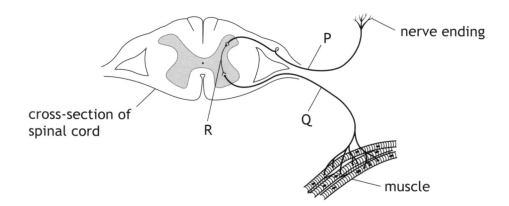

Which row in the table identifies P, Q and R?

	Motor neuron	Sensory neuron	Inter neuron
A	Q	R	P
B	Q	P	R
C	R	P	Q
D	P	R	Q

10. The diagram represents a section through the brain.

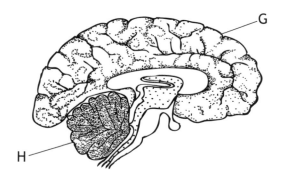

Which of the following links a letter to its correct structure and function?

A   G is the cerebrum and is the site of reasoning and memory.

B   G is the cerebellum and is the site of reasoning and memory.

C   H is the medulla and controls muscle coordination.

D   H is the cerebellum and controls breathing and heart rate.

Questions 11 and 12 refer to the following flow diagram related to blood glucose regulation.

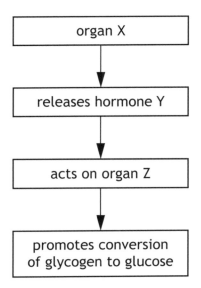

11. Which row in the table identifies organ X and hormone Y?

	Organ X	Hormone Y
A	Liver	Insulin
B	Liver	Glucagon
C	Pancreas	Insulin
D	Pancreas	Glucagon

12. Specialised cells allow organ Z to respond to hormone Y.

This is because the surface of the cells in organ Z have complementary

A   synapses

B   neurons

C   effectors

D   receptors.

[Turn over

13. An **increase** in which of the following factors would **decrease** the rate of transpiration in plants?

    A   Wind speed

    B   Humidity

    C   Surface area

    D   Temperature

14. Which of the following statements about blood cells is **false**?

    A   White blood cells are part of the immune system.

    B   Phagocytes are a type of white blood cell.

    C   Red blood cells contain haemoglobin.

    D   Phagocytes transport nutrients around the body.

15. Which row in the table identifies how lymphocytes destroy pathogens?

	Antibody production	Phagocytosis
A	Yes	No
B	No	No
C	No	Yes
D	Yes	Yes

16. The following key can be used to identify the different components of blood.

1.	Nucleus absent	go to 2
	Nucleus present	go to 3
2.	Diameter greater than 0·005 mm	**red blood cell**
	Diameter less than 0·005 mm	**platelet**
3.	Nucleus is circular	**lymphocyte**
	Nucleus is not circular	**macrophage**

Use the key above to identify which of the diagrams represents a platelet.

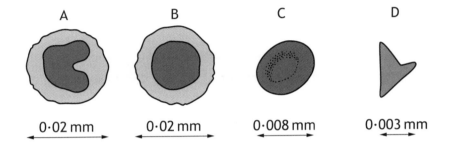

A   B   C   D

0·02 mm   0·02 mm   0·008 mm   0·003 mm

17. Which of the following statements is true of villi?

A   Blood capillaries absorb glycerol and amino acids.

B   Blood capillaries absorb glucose and fatty acids.

C   Lacteals absorb glycerol and fatty acids.

D   Lacteals absorb glucose and amino acids.

18. An ecosystem consists of abiotic factors plus a

A   community and its biodiversity

B   population and its biodiversity

C   population and its habitat

D   community and its habitat.

[Turn over

19. The diagram shows part of a food web.

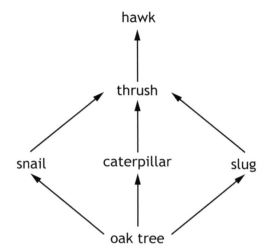

A chemical was used to control the number of slugs.

Which of the following could be a result of a large decrease in slug numbers?

A   An increase in snails.

B   An increase in hawks.

C   A decrease in caterpillars.

D   A decrease in oak trees.

20. The diagrams show an investigation into seed germination.

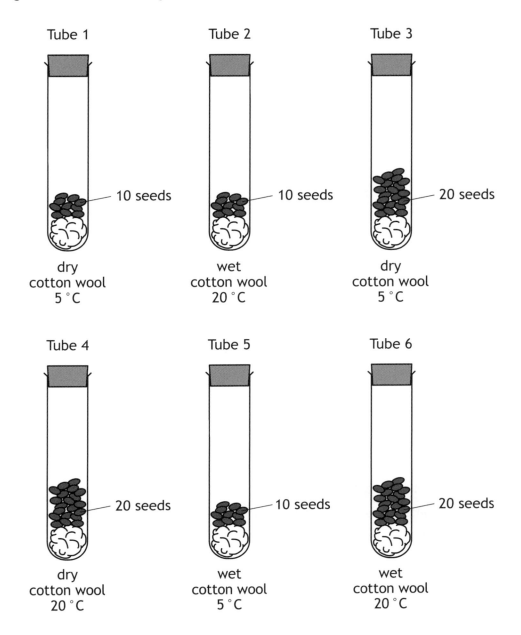

For a valid conclusion to be drawn, which two tubes should be compared to show the effect of temperature on germination?

A   1 and 3

B   3 and 6

C   2 and 5

D   4 and 6

[Turn over

21. The diagram represents a pyramid of energy.

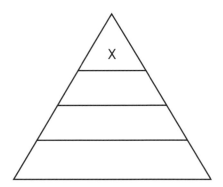

There is less energy at level X in the pyramid because

A   there are fewer organisms at each level in the food chain

B   the organisms at level X are very small

C   energy is lost at each level in the food chain

D   energy is stored in each level and not passed on.

22. Mutations result in changes to genetic material.

Which of the following is **not** true of mutations?

A   Radiation can increase their rate.

B   They always have a harmful effect.

C   Genetic material is affected at random.

D   New alleles may be produced.

23. Natural selection occurs when there are selection pressures.

Which of the following could be a result of selection pressures?

A   Organisms with favourable alleles survive and reproduce.

B   Organisms with new alleles always have an advantage.

C   All alleles in a population increase in frequency.

D   All alleles in a population decrease in frequency.

24. Pesticides sprayed onto crops can get into food chains. The following statements refer to stages in this process.

    J   Pesticides are absorbed by plants.

    K   Pesticides build up in animals.

    L   Plants are eaten by animals.

    Identify the order of steps by which pesticides could reach lethal levels in the bodies of animals.

	Step 1	Step 2	Step 3
A	J	K	L
B	L	J	K
C	L	K	J
D	J	L	K

25. Which row in the table identifies biotic and abiotic factors which can affect a population?

	Biotic factors	Abiotic factors
A	grazing and predation	pH and temperature
B	predation and temperature	pH and grazing
C	pH and temperature	grazing and predation
D	pH and grazing	predation and temperature

[END OF SECTION 1. NOW ATTEMPT THE QUESTIONS IN SECTION 2 OF YOUR QUESTION AND ANSWER BOOKLET.]

[BLANK PAGE]

DO NOT WRITE ON THIS PAGE

Mark

N5

National
Qualifications
2018

X807/75/01

Biology
Section 1—Answer Grid
and Section 2

TUESDAY, 15 MAY
1:00 PM – 3:30 PM

Fill in these boxes and read what is printed below.

Full name of centre

Town

Forename(s)

Surname

Number of seat

Date of birth

Day   Month   Year   Scottish candidate number

Total marks — 100

SECTION 1 — 25 marks

Attempt ALL questions.

Instructions for the completion of Section 1 are given on *Page two*.

SECTION 2 — 75 marks

Attempt ALL questions.

Write your answers clearly in the spaces provided in this booklet. Additional space for answers and rough work is provided at the end of this booklet. If you use this space you must clearly identify the question number you are attempting. Any rough work must be written in this booklet. Score through your rough work when you have written your final copy.

Use **blue** or **black** ink.

Before leaving the examination room you must give this booklet to the Invigilator; if you do not, you may lose all the marks for this paper.

SECTION 1 — 25 marks

The questions for Section 1 are contained in the question paper X807/75/02.

Read these and record your answers on the answer grid on *Page three* opposite.

Use **blue** or **black** ink. Do NOT use gel pens or pencil.

1. The answer to each question is **either** A, B, C or D. Decide what your answer is, then fill in the appropriate bubble (see sample question below).

2. There is **only one correct** answer to each question.

3. Any rough working should be done on the additional space for answers and rough work at the end of this booklet.

Sample question

The thigh bone is called the

     A   humerus

     B   femur

     C   tibia

     D   fibula.

The correct answer is **B** — femur. The answer **B** bubble has been clearly filled in (see below).

Changing an answer

If you decide to change your answer, cancel your first answer by putting a cross through it (see below) and fill in the answer you want. The answer below has been changed to **D**.

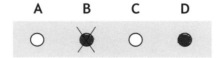

If you then decide to change back to an answer you have already scored out, put a tick (✓) to the **right** of the answer you want, as shown below:

or

SECTION 1 — Answer Grid

	A	B	C	D
1	○	○	○	○
2	○	○	○	○
3	○	○	○	○
4	○	○	○	○
5	○	○	○	○
6	○	○	○	○
7	○	○	○	○
8	○	○	○	○
9	○	○	○	○
10	○	○	○	○
11	○	○	○	○
12	○	○	○	○
13	○	○	○	○
14	○	○	○	○
15	○	○	○	○
16	○	○	○	○
17	○	○	○	○
18	○	○	○	○
19	○	○	○	○
20	○	○	○	○
21	○	○	○	○
22	○	○	○	○
23	○	○	○	○
24	○	○	○	○
25	○	○	○	○

MARKS | DO NOT WRITE IN THIS MARGIN

SECTION 2 — 75 marks

Attempt ALL questions

1. (a) The diagram shows a typical animal cell and some of its structures.

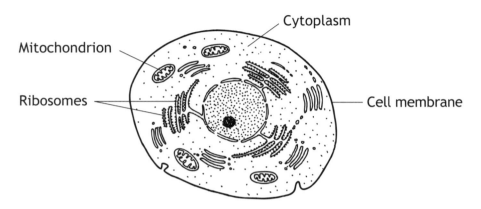

Choose **two** of the structures labelled and state their functions.   2

1 Structure _____

   Function _____

   _____

2 Structure _____

   Function _____

   _____

   (b) The field of view of a light microscope measures 2 mm in diameter.

   20 plant cells were counted in a line across the diameter.

   1 mm = 1000 micrometres

   Calculate the average size of a cell in micrometres.   1

   Space for calculation

   _____ micrometres

MARKS | DO NOT WRITE IN THIS MARGIN

2. A student examined plant and animal cells using a microscope.

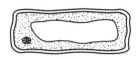

Animal cell   Plant cell

The animal and plant cells were placed in solutions of different salt concentrations. After several minutes a sample of cells was taken from each solution and examined. One cell from each solution is shown.

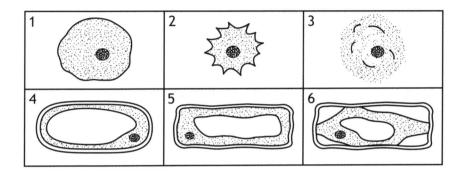

(a) Changes in the cells were due to osmosis.

Explain why osmosis is described as a passive process.   1

_____

_____

(b) Identify the animal cell shown which had been placed in a solution of higher salt concentration than its cell contents.   1

Cell number _____

(c) State the term used to describe the condition of cell 6.   1

_____

(d) Cells 3 and 4 had been placed in solutions which were both of the same concentration.

Explain why the results observed were different.   2

_____

_____

_____

MARKS | DO NOT WRITE IN THIS MARGIN

3. The diagram represents part of a DNA molecule.

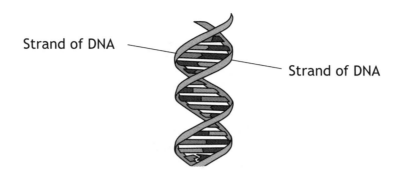

Strand of DNA

Strand of DNA

(a) (i) Give the term which describes the shape of a DNA molecule as shown in the diagram.   **1**

_____

(ii) Describe the way in which the DNA strands are linked together.   **1**

_____

(b) Name the organelle in animal cells which stores the DNA.   **1**

_____

MARKS | DO NOT WRITE IN THIS MARGIN

4.   The diagrams represent stages in an enzyme-controlled reaction.

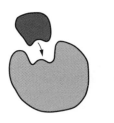  

Stage 1   Stage 2   Stage 3

(a) Enzymes are involved in two types of reaction.

Identify the type of reaction shown in the diagrams above.   **1**

_____

(b) Describe the events occurring in the enzyme reaction shown.   **3**

_____

_____

_____

_____

_____

_____

_____

_____

_____

_____

[Turn over

MARKS DO NOT WRITE IN THIS MARGIN

5. (a) The table shows information about two types of respiration in animal cells.

Tick the boxes in the table to indicate whether the statements apply to aerobic respiration, fermentation or both.   **2**

Statement	Type of respiration	
	Aerobic	Fermentation
Oxygen is required		
Pyruvate is formed		
Lactate is formed		
Carbon dioxide is formed		

(b) ATP is an energy-rich molecule formed by respiration.

Name a cellular process which requires energy from ATP.   **1**

_____

6. An investigation was carried out into the effect of pH on the activity of the enzyme pepsin.

   A Petri dish was filled with cloudy protein agar. Six holes were made in the agar and each was filled with pepsin solution at the pH values shown.

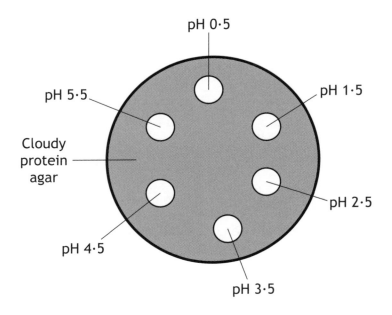

When the protein is broken down, cloudy agar becomes clear.

The dish was examined after 24 hours and the diameter of the clear area around each hole was measured. The larger the clear area, the more active the enzyme.

The results are shown in the graph.

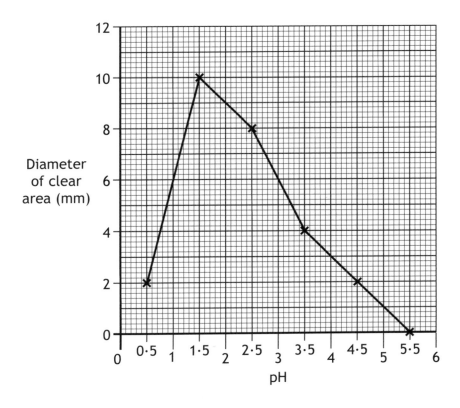

MARKS | DO NOT WRITE IN THIS MARGIN

6.   (continued)

(a)   (i)   Identify the optimum pH for pepsin in this experiment.   1

pH _____

(ii)   Calculate how many times more active the enzyme is at pH 2·5 than at pH 4·5.   1

Space for calculation

_____ times

(b)   State two variables which should be controlled to make this experiment valid.   2

1 _____

2 _____

(c)   As a follow-up to this investigation, students were asked to design an experiment using the same apparatus to identify a more exact optimum pH value.

Complete the diagram below to show the pH values the students could use.   1

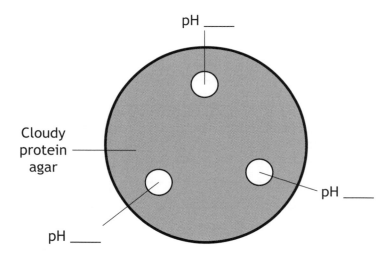

MARKS | DO NOT WRITE IN THIS MARGIN

7. The process of mitosis begins with the chromosomes becoming visible.

Describe the sequence of events which follows on from this resulting in the production of two daughter cells.

4

_____

_____

_____

_____

_____

_____

_____

_____

_____

_____

_____

[Turn over

MARKS | DO NOT WRITE IN THIS MARGIN

8. The diagrams show the human reproductive system in females and males.

Female   **Male**

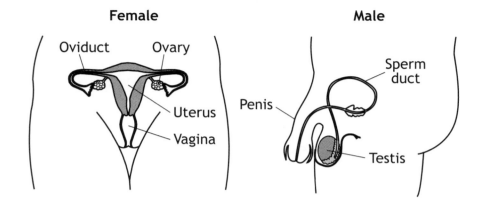

(a) From the diagrams, identify **one** site of gamete production.   1

_____

(b) The diagram represents the process of fertilisation.

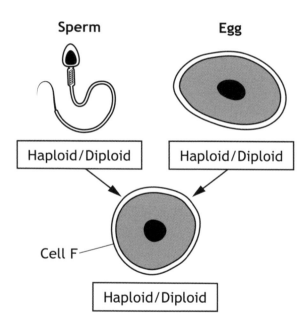

(i) In the diagram, circle one term in each box to show the chromosome complement for each cell.   1

(ii) Name cell F which is produced when the sperm fertilises the egg.   1

_____

MARKS | DO NOT WRITE IN THIS MARGIN

9.

Adapted from the Herald, Friday 4 March 2016

Coffee and Multiple Sclerosis

Multiple sclerosis (MS) is a condition which affects the central nervous system and can cause problems with vision and balance as well as numbness in the skin. Scotland has one of the highest incidences of MS in the world, with a mixture of genetic and environmental factors thought to be the cause.

Research suggests that drinking a lot of coffee every day could potentially cut the risk of developing MS.

Experts found that consuming more than 900 ml daily may offer up to 30% reduced risk.

Researchers compared the results of studies from two different countries.

One study in Sweden involved 1,620 adults with MS and a comparison group of 2,788 people without MS. A second study in the USA involved 1,159 people with MS and 1,172 people without MS.

The results showed the risk of MS was consistently higher among people who drank fewer cups of coffee every day in both studies, even after taking into account other factors of influence.

(a) Identify the factors thought to be the cause of the high incidence of MS in Scotland.

1

_____

(b) In the table below, present the information from the passage, to give details of the two studies and the people involved.

2

(An additional table, if required, can be found on *Page twenty-seven*.)

Country		

[Turn over

MARKS | DO NOT WRITE IN THIS MARGIN

9.   (continued)

(c) As part of the research described in the passage, groups of people with MS were compared to those without MS.

Give the term used to describe a comparison group in scientific research.   **1**

_____

(d) Decide whether this research would be described as reliable or not and tick the appropriate box.

Give a reason for your choice.   **1**

Reliable ☐   Not reliable ☐

Reason _____

_____

_____

(e) The researcher took 'other factors of influence' into consideration.

Suggest one of these factors.   **1**

_____

MARKS | DO NOT WRITE IN THIS MARGIN

10. The following statements are about blood vessels.

1. Contain valves.

2. Have a narrow central channel.

3. Carry blood under low pressure.

4. Form networks at organs and tissues.

5. Carry blood from the heart to organs.

(a) Choose either arteries or veins and select two statements from the list above which describe that type of blood vessel.   **2**

Blood vessel _____

Statements _____ and _____

(b) The graph shows the effect of changes in heart rate on the volume of blood pumped by the left ventricle.

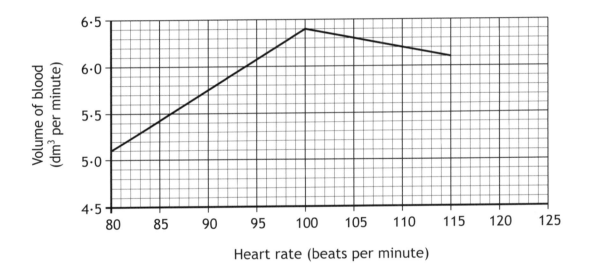

(i) Describe the relationship between heart rate and volume of blood pumped by the left ventricle.   **2**

_____

_____

(ii) Predict the volume of blood pumped by the left ventricle at 120 beats per minute.   **1**

_____ dm³ per minute

[Turn over

MARKS | DO NOT WRITE IN THIS MARGIN

10.   (continued)

(c)   The diagram represents part of the circulatory system in humans.

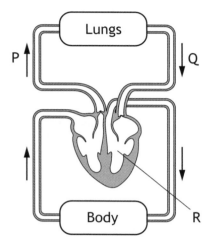

(i)   Describe the difference in oxygen concentration in the blood travelling through blood vessels P and Q.   **1**

_____

_____

(ii)   Name the heart chamber labelled R.   **1**

_____

MARKS | DO NOT WRITE IN THIS MARGIN

11. (a) Tongue-rolling is an inherited characteristic controlled by different forms of a gene. T (roller) represents the dominant form of the gene, and t (non-roller) represents the recessive form.

The family tree diagram shows a pattern of inheritance of the characteristic.

○ Male tongue-roller   ● Male non tongue-roller

□ Female tongue-roller   ■ Female non tongue-roller

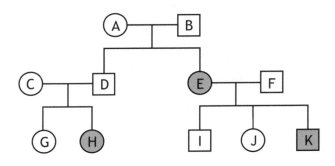

(i) Use letters from the diagram to identify all the individuals in the F₂ generation.

1

_____

(ii) Give the genotypes of individuals E and F.

2

E _____   F _____

(iii) Complete the Punnett square to show the gametes and expected genotypes of the offspring of E and F.

2

	Genotype of gametes from F	
Genotype of gametes from E		

(b) State the type of variation shown by tongue-rolling.

1

_____

[Turn over

MARKS | DO NOT WRITE IN THIS MARGIN

12. The diagram represents a section through a leaf.

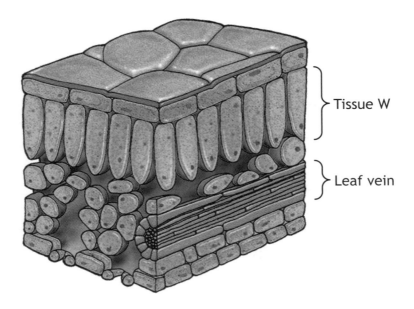

Tissue W

Leaf vein

(a) (i) Name tissue W.   **1**

_____

(ii) The cells in tissue W have a greater number of chloroplasts than other leaf cells.

Suggest the advantage of these cells being located near the upper surface of the leaf.   **1**

_____

_____

(b) The leaf vein consists of xylem and phloem tissues.

Choose either xylem or phloem, by ticking one box, and describe one structural feature of that tissue.   **1**

Xylem ☐   Phloem ☐

Feature of tissue _____

_____

MARKS | DO NOT WRITE IN THIS MARGIN

13. To investigate the effect of competition on the growth of cress seeds, five Petri dishes, labelled A-E, were set up and left for six days. Each dish contained a layer of moist cotton wool with different numbers of cress seeds sown evenly across its surface.

Dish A is shown in the diagram.

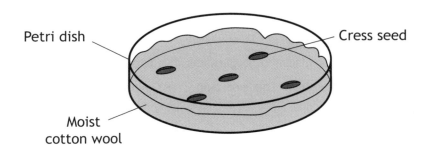

Petri dish   Cress seed

Moist
cotton wool

The results are shown in the table.

Dish	Number of seeds sown	Number of seedlings surviving after six days	Percentage of seedlings surviving after six days
A	5	5	100
B	10	10	100
C	20		95
D	40	34	85
E	80	60	75

(a) (i) Complete the table by calculating the number of seedlings surviving in Dish C.   1

Space for calculation

(ii) Describe the relationship between the number of seeds sown and the percentage of seedlings surviving after six days.   1

_____

_____

[Turn over

MARKS | DO NOT WRITE IN THIS MARGIN

13. **(a)** **(continued)**

(iii) Explain why the type of competition shown in this investigation is described as being intraspecific.

1

_____

_____

(b) The diagram represents positions of organisms in a food chain.

Tick one of the boxes to show the position cress would occupy in the food chain.

1

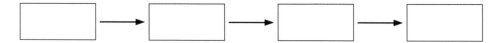

(c) Name one resource, other than water, for which plants may be in competition.

1

_____

MARKS | DO NOT WRITE IN THIS MARGIN

14. Sampling techniques can be used to estimate the abundance of plants and animals.

(a) In an investigation into ground-living animals in a woodland, a group of students collected and counted the animals they found.

    (i) Name a sampling technique which could be used to collect the ground-living animals.

        1

_____

    (ii) The students sorted the animals into male and female, counted them and recorded the results in a bar graph.

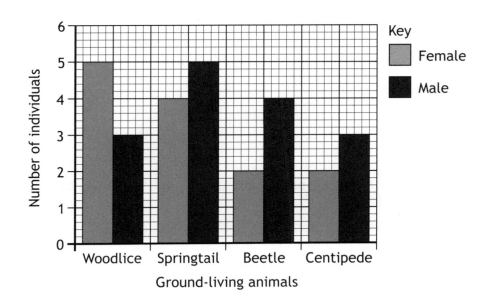

      1   Identify the animal which had the greatest overall abundance.   1

    _____

      2   The students concluded that males were always more abundant than females.

          Identify the animal for which this is **not** true.   1

    _____

    (iii) It was decided that the samples were not fully representative of the area.

       Suggest how the investigation could be improved.   1

_____

_____

[Turn over

MARKS | DO NOT WRITE IN THIS MARGIN

14. (continued)

(b) The distribution of organisms may be affected by abiotic factors.

The table shows the results of a study into the effect of soil moisture levels on the distribution of three species of plant.

Sample site	Soil moisture (units)	Number of plants		
		Species E	Species F	Species G
1	20·2	11	15	12
2	23·4	13	14	11
3	22·1	12	16	10
4	24·5	15	17	15
5	26·6	18	13	12
6	28·4	19	15	14

(i) State which species has its distribution most affected by the soil moisture levels.   1

Species _____

(ii) Calculate the average number of plants per sample site for species F.   1

Space for calculation

_____ plants

MARKS | DO NOT WRITE IN THIS MARGIN

15. A student set up an investigation into the effect of temperature on the rate of photosynthesis in a green plant, by measuring the volume of oxygen released in one hour.

The results are shown in the table.

Temperature (°C)	Volume of oxygen released in one hour (cm³)		
	Experiment 1	Experiment 2	Average
10	0·7	0·5	0·6
20	1·6	1·4	1·5
30	2·7	1·9	2·3
40	2·0	2·6	2·3
50	0·3	0·5	0·4

(a) On the grid, plot a line graph to show the effect of temperature on the average volume of oxygen released in one hour.

(An additional grid, if required, can be found on *Page twenty-seven.*)

2

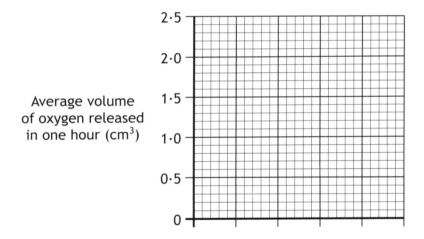

(b) Predict the average volume of oxygen released in one hour if the experiment was carried out at a temperature of 60 °C.

1

_____ cm³

[**Turn over**

MARKS | DO NOT WRITE IN THIS MARGIN

15.   (continued)

(c)   State one factor, other than temperature, which can limit the rate of photosynthesis.

1

_____

(d)   The diagram represents the second stage of photosynthesis.

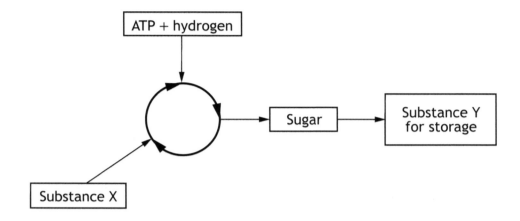

Name substances X and Y.

2

X _____

Y _____

16. A gardener treated the soil in the area where he planted veg
chemical to increase the yield.

(a)   (i)   The chemical added to the soil by the gardener contai

Give the general name for this type of chemical.

_____

(ii) Describe the use that plants make of nitrates.

_____

(iii) When the vegetables were picked and weighed, the total yield was
42 kilograms. The previous year the total yield was 35 kilograms.

Calculate the percentage increase in yield.   1

Space for calculation

_____ %

[Turn over

MARKS | DO NOT WRITE IN THIS MARGIN

(continued)

(b) Later in the year the gardener noticed that the algae in his pond had increased and now covered the surface of the water. He sampled the pond water over 5 weeks and measured its oxygen concentration and number of bacteria present.

The results are shown in the graph.

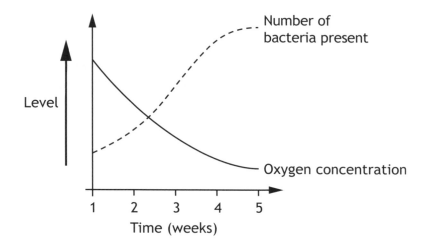

(i) What name is given to the increased growth of algae in the pond? **1**

_____

(ii) Explain why the increased growth of algae resulted in an increase in the number of bacteria. **1**

_____

_____

(iii) Using the information in the graph, explain why the increase in number of bacteria resulted in the population of goldfish in the pond decreasing. **1**

_____

_____

[END OF QUESTION PAPER]

MARKS | DO NOT WRITE IN THIS MARGIN

ADDITIONAL SPACE FOR ANSWERS AND ROUGH WORK

Additional table for Question 9 (b)

Country		

Additional grid for Question 15 (a)

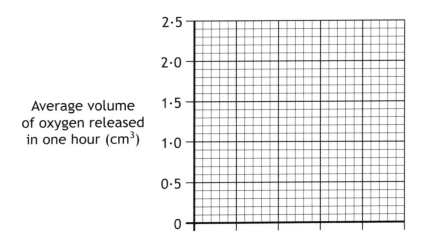

MARKS | DO NOT WRITE IN THIS MARGIN

ADDITIONAL SPACE FOR ANSWERS AND ROUGH WORK

Page twenty-eight

NATIONAL 5

Answers

NATIONAL 5 BIOLOGY 2017

SECTION 1

Question	Response
1.	B
2.	D
3.	A
4.	B
5.	B
6.	B
7.	D
8.	C
9.	D
10.	A
11.	A
12.	C
13.	B
14.	A
15.	C
16.	C
17.	D
18.	C
19.	B
20.	C

SECTION 2

1. (a) (i) Cytoplasm — site of (chemical) reactions
OR
Cell membrane — controls/allows/lets entry and/or exit/passage of materials/substances/molecules
OR
Controls what enters/exits
OR
Nucleus — controls (all) cell activity/activities

    (ii) Osmosis

  (b) Cell wall

2. (a) (i) ☐3☐ Pairs of chromatids are pulled apart

    (ii) Spindle (fibre)

  (b) 40

3. (a) 1 = cytosine
2 = thymine

  (b) Sequence/order of bases

  (c) Messenger RNA/mRNA/MRNA

4. (a) Appropriate scale and label **(1)**
Scale must have 0, 108 or 120 and one other number in between

Label — Time (taken) for disc(s) to return to (the) surface s/seconds
Bars correctly plotted **(1)**

  (b) Liver has the highest catalase activity/apple has the lowest catalase activity/different tissues have different catalase activity/animal tissue has higher catalase activity (than plants) or other appropriate conclusion

  (c) Decrease

5. (a) (i) 1·3

    (ii) Temperature

    (iii) (Respiration is) controlled by enzymes/enzymes are needed **(1)**
Enzymes have been denatured (at 60°C) or description of denatured **(1)**

    (iv) To show it is the **germinating/live** peas that are producing the result/using oxygen/respiring
OR
To show that <u>dead</u> peas do not respire

  (b) X — Pyruvate
OR
Y — Ethanol/alcohol

6. (a) Discrete **(1)**
Heterozygous **(1)**

  (b) (i) Testis/testes

    (ii) Sperm <u>nucleus</u> and egg <u>nucleus</u> fuse or join together/sperm and egg <u>nuclei</u> fuse/gamete <u>nuclei</u> fuse or join together

    (iii) Haploid cell or egg has half the number of chromosomes
OR
Diploid cell or zygote has double/twice the number of chromosomes
OR
Haploid cell or egg has one set of chromosomes/23 chromosomes whereas diploid cell or zygote has two sets of chromosomes/46 chromosomes

7. (a) 11:7

  (b) (i) Oxygen/nutrients/glucose/amino acids

    (ii) Reduce/stop smoking
Reduce fat in diet/cholesterol in diet/salt intake/sugar intake/alcohol intake/stress
Lose weight/healthier diet/healthier eating

  (c) (Large) surface area/(rich) blood supply/(dense) capillary network

8. (a) 150

  (b) (i) Will be less evaporation/water loss
OR
Plant will not require as much water

    (ii) Dry

9. (a) Cerebellum

  (b) 1. Detected by <u>receptors</u> **(1)**

    2. Sent by <u>electrical</u> impulse/signal **(1)**

3. (Message/information/impulse goes) from sensory to relay neuron/

sensory ————→ relay neuron **(1)**

4. Across synapse
OR
Chemical transfer between neurons **(1)**

10. (a) (i) Pancreas

(ii) Glucose is needed to release/give out <u>energy</u>
OR
If cells do not have glucose they release/give out less/no <u>energy</u>

(b) (i) S

(ii) P

(c) Receptor (protein)

11. (a) Set up more than one field for each variety/
Repeat the (whole) investigation/
Use more potatoes/plants in each field

(b) 175

(c) Number of potatoes/plants
Spacing between potatoes/plants
pH of soil
Nutrient content of soil
Moisture content of soil
Fertility of soil
Type of soil

(d) Pesticides/insecticides/predator/biological control/crop rotation

12. (a) Niche

(b) Mutation

(c) (Offspring would be) infertile/sterile

13.

Statement	True	False	Correction
Genetic variation within a population allows the population to <u>adapt</u> in a changing environment.	✓		
Isolation barriers can be geographical, <u>environmental</u> or reproductive.		✓	Ecological
Sub-populations evolve until they become genetically <u>identical</u>.		✓	Non-identical/ varied/different

14. (a) (i) Nitrites

(ii) 3
OR
4

(b) (i) Plants/producers/denitrifying bacteria

(ii) To make protein/amino acids

(c) Fungi

15. (a) (i) Has most crusty lichen and these are common/found in high pollution

(ii) 6

(b) Indicator (species)

SECTION 1

Question	Answer
1.	B
2.	D
3.	A
4.	A
5.	C
6.	B
7.	D
8.	C
9.	B
10.	C
11.	A
12.	D
13.	A
14.	D
15.	A
16.	B
17.	C
18.	A
19.	D
20.	B
21.	B
22.	D
23.	C
24.	B
25.	C

SECTION 2

1. (a) Y

(b) Large number of mitochondria present

(c) Chloroplasts present **(1)**

Contain chlorophyll/green pigment/are green **(1)**

2. (a) (i) From cell of alveolus wall to cell of capillary wall to red blood cell

(ii) (Oxygen) moves from a higher concentration to a lower concentration or down a concentration gradient

(b) There is no concentration gradient/difference in concentration/concentration equal in all cells

3. (a) (i) mRNA/messenger RNA

(ii) Bases **(1)**
C **(1)**

(b) Gene

(c) Different sequence/order of bases

4. (a) (i) Arginine

(ii) Lysine

(iii) Serine

(b) 1·3

(c) Appropriate scale — must have 0, 6.4, 7 or 8 and at least one other number in between **(1)**

Bars correctly plotted with clear bar tops **(1)**

5. (a) Carbon dioxide

(b) pH 5 **(1)**

Highest (average) number of bubbles (for most groups) **(1)**

(c) All flasks at same pH **(1)**

Any one from:
Yeast — different types of yeast in each flask
OR
Temperature — different temperatures
OR
Glucose — different glucose concentrations used **(1)**

6. (a) B A C E (D)

All required to be correct

(b) (Pairs of) chromatids/chromosomes line up at equator/centre (of the cell)

(Must have reference to what lines up and where)

(c) To maintain the (diploid) chromosome complement/ so no genetic information is lost/so the daughter/ new cells contain the same genetic information as the original cell

(d) 7

7. (a) (i) Target cell has complementary receptor (proteins) for the hormone/the hormone fits the receptor (proteins) on the target cells only/ the hormone and receptor (proteins) have complementary shapes

(ii) Any one difference:

Hormone message — chemical/long-lasting/ carried in blood/carried all over body
Nerve message — electrical/short-lived effect/ carried along specific nerves/path

(Must be comparative between hormone and nerve)

(b) (i) Type 1

Insulin not produced

(Both parts needed)

(ii) Would stay higher than normal/would stay too high

(iii) Pancreas

8. (a) Heterozygous

(b)

	H	h
H	HH	Hh
h	Hh	hh

(All parts must be correct)

(c) HH and Hh

(Both are needed)

9. (a) To prevent water evaporating/being lost from the soil (which will affect the weight/mass)

(b) 1·41

(c) Exactly the same set up but without the plant

(d) Decrease

(e) Stomata/stoma

10. (a) Choose any two of arteries, veins and capillaries

Comparison of:
Thickness of walls
Muscularity of walls
Presence and absence of valves
Size of channel for blood flow

Any three for 3 marks

(Must compare chosen blood vessels and refer to structural differences)

(b) Carries oxygen

11. (a) (i) Mouths are all different shapes/sizes/structures

(ii) A, B, D (any two)

(b) Niche

(c) (3)-1-5-4-2

(All required to be correct)

(d) All the organisms living in a particular area and the non-living components (with which they interact)

12. (a) (i) Hydrogen

(ii) Light energy is trapped by chlorophyll **(1)**

Light energy/it is converted into chemical energy in ATP **(1)**

(Energy stored in sugar can be used for) respiration/converted into cellulose or starch or any other correctly named substance/protein synthesis or cell division or any other named plant process **(1)**

(b) Light intensity **(1)**
Carbon dioxide concentration **(1)**

13. (a) To find out if drinking beetroot/nitrate-rich juice affects sprint **and** decision making performance

(Both parts needed)

(b) (sprint and decision making) performance

(c)

Sprint test/Activities	Time/Timing (seconds)
Sprint	10
Slow pedalling	80
Rest	30

Suitable headings with appropriate units **(1)**
All information given in columns of table **(1)**

(d) Drinking nitrate-rich (beetroot) juice gives an (3·5%) improvement in sprint performance **and** an (3%) increase in their speed of making decisions

(e) Only used males/too small a sample/only tested on people involved in two sports

14. (a) L

(b) Shows the total available energy of the living organisms/population at each stage/level in a food chain

(c) Heat/movement/undigested material

15. (a) Initial populations all had different starting sizes

(b) 4·3

(c) Starling and yellow wagtail

(Both needed)

16. (a) (As you move from sample site 1 to sample site 5,) the abundance of Yellow Iris increases/it increases

(b) Soil moisture

(c) Wipe/dry the probe between samples
OR
Probe at the same depth each time

17. (a) Long and thin **(1)**
Egg wrack **(1)**
Bladder wrack **(1)**

(b) Egg wrack has bladders present along its length whereas Bladder wrack's (bladders) are in pairs

(Comparison needed)

(c) Brown or no bladders

NATIONAL 5 BIOLOGY 2018

SECTION 1

Question	Answer
1.	B
2.	C
3.	D
4.	B
5.	C
6.	D
7.	B
8.	C
9.	B
10.	A
11.	D
12.	D
13.	B
14.	D
15.	A
16.	D
17.	C
18.	D
19.	A
20.	C
21.	C
22.	B
23.	A
24.	D
25.	A

SECTION 2

1. (a) 1. Mitochondrion:
(site of) <u>aerobic</u> respiration
or
releases energy/produces ATP.

2. Cytoplasm:
(site of) chemical reactions.

3. Ribosome(s):
(site of) protein synthesis.

4. Cell membrane:
controls or allows entry/exit of materials/substances/molecules
or
controls what enters/exits.
Any 2 for 1 mark each

(b) 100

2. (a) Does not require energy/ATP.

(b) 2

(c) Plasmolysed

(d) Plant cells/cell 4 have a cell wall
or
animal cells/cell 3 do not have a cell wall. **(1)**
Cell wall prevents cells from bursting/no cell wall so cell bursts. **(1)**

3. (a) (i) Double (stranded) helix
(ii) Complementary bases
or
base pairs/base pairing
or
adenine pairs with thymine **and** cytosine pairs with guanine.

(b) <u>Nucleus</u>

4. (a) Degradation/breakdown

(b) 1. Enzyme and substrate join/fit/bind together
OR
substrate joins/fits/binds with active site
OR
enzyme-substrate complex forms
OR
enzyme and substrate are complementary/specific. **(1)**

2. Reaction occurs at <u>active site</u> of the enzyme
OR
enzyme has an <u>active site</u>. **(1)**

3. (Two/smaller) <u>product</u>(s) made/formed/released. **(1)**
Do not award mark for point 3 if description relates to synthesis reaction

5. (a)

Statement	Aerobic	Fermentation
Oxygen is required	✓	
Pyruvate is formed	✓	✓
Lactate is formed		✓
Carbon dioxide is formed	✓	

(1)   **(1)**

(b) Muscle contraction/cell division/protein synthesis/transmission of nerve impulses/active transport.
Acceptable:
carbon fixation or any other correctly named example

6. (a) (i) 1·5
(ii) 4

(b) Temperature
Volume of pepsin/solution
Concentration of pepsin
Spacing of holes
Size/depth/diameter/volume of holes/wells
Any two for 1 mark each

(c) Three values **between** 0·5 and 2·5 ensuring that there are values above and below the optimum (1·5).

7. 1. Chromosomes/chromatids move to/line up at/across the equator. **(1)**

    2. Spindle (fibres) form/attach/contract/shorten/pull. **(1)**

    3. (Pairs of) chromatids are separated/pulled apart. **(1)**

    4. Chromosomes move to poles/opposite ends of cell. **(1)**

    5. Nuclear membrane(s) form/develop
       OR
       2 nuclei form. **(1)**

    6. Cytoplasm divides/splits. **(1)**

    Any 4 marks from 6 but *must* include point 3 and any other three points to get full marks

8. (a) Testis
       OR
       Ovary

    Singular or plural accepted

    (b) (i) Haploid — Haploid
           Diploid

        (ii) Zygote

9. (a) (Mixture of) genetics and environment(al).

    (b) Suitable headings for the columns and rows (either order). **(1)**

        Correct values included in table **(1)**
        (in the absence of suitable headings this mark can be accessed if the context of the values can still be determined).

    (c) Control (group)

    (d) Reliable:
        — as there was a large number of people involved
        — two countries were used (rather than one).
        OR
        Not reliable:
        — as there were **only** two countries/studies involved.

    (e) Any reasonable answer about the people chosen eg gender, diet, age, health issues, drug use, smoking
        OR
        about the conditions of the trial eg strength of coffee, time over which it was consumed etc.

10. (a) Arteries: 2 and 5
       OR
       Veins: 1 and 3

    1 mark for each correct number

    (b) (i) As the heart rate increases the volume of blood (pumped) increases until 100(bpm) and then decreases.

        (ii) 6·0/6

    (c) (i) Higher/more in Q (than in P)
           OR
           Lower/less in P (than in Q)
           OR
           High in Q **and** low in P

        (ii) Left ventricle

11. (a) (i) G, H, I, J, K
           Need all 5 to obtain mark

        (ii) E: tt
             F: Tt

        (iii)

	T	t
t	Tt	tt
t	Tt	tt

        1 mark for gametes
        1 mark for offspring genotypes

    (b) Discrete

12. (a) (i) Palisade mesophyll

        (ii) To absorb/capture/trap **more** light

    (b) Xylem:
        lignin/hollow/no cell contents/no end walls.

        Phloem:
        sieve plates/sieve tubes/companion cells.

        Any description of function must be related to the structural feature given

13. (a) (i) 19

        (ii) (Up to 10 seeds sown, the percentage of seedlings surviving remains constant and thereafter) as the number of seeds (sown) increases the percentage (of seedlings) surviving decreases.

            Also acceptable:
            as the number of seeds (sown) decreases the percentage (of seedlings) surviving increases (until 10 seeds and then it remains constant)

        (iii) They/plants/seeds/seedlings/organisms are the same species.

    (b) Tick in first box.

    (c) Light/sunlight/nutrients/minerals/space.

14. (a) (i) Pitfall trap

        (ii) 1. Springtail **(1)**
             2. Woodlice **(1)**

        (iii) Set several traps.
              Check traps more often.
              Repeat the investigation/experiment.
              Not acceptable: repeat in different areas.

    (b) (i) E
        (ii) 15

15. (a) X-axis scale and label including units. **(1)**
       Plotting and joining points accurately. **(1)**

    (b) Any value **less than** 0·4 (including 0).

    (c) Light intensity/carbon dioxide concentration.

    (d) Substance X — carbon dioxide/CO_2 **(1)**
        Substance Y — starch **(1)**

16. (a) (i) Fertiliser

        (ii) To make protein/amino acids.

        (iii) 20

    (b) (i) (Algal) bloom

        (ii) Bacteria have more food/more algae to feed on.

        (iii) Drop in oxygen concentration/lower oxygen concentration/less oxygen for fish due to bacteria using up oxygen.

Acknowledgements

Permission has been sought from all relevant copyright holders and Hodder Gibson is grateful for the use of the following:

Image © Rahul Alvares/Shutterstock.com (2017 Section 2 page 22);
Image © Margarita Borodina/Shutterstock.com (2017 SQP Section 2 page 15);
Article is adapted from "Beetroot juice boosts your decision making," taken from 'The Herald', Saturday 19th September 2015. Reproduced by permission of Newsquest Media Group (2017 SQP Section 2 page 22);
Image © Elena Blokhina/Shutterstock.com (2017 SQP Section 2 page 26);
Article is adapted from "Coffee and Multiple Sclerosis" taken from 'The Herald', Friday 4th March 2016. Reproduced by permission of Newsquest Media Group (2018 Section 2 page 13);
Diagram from www.digitalfrog.com/resources/archives/leaf.jpg is reproduced by permission of Digital Frog International (2018 Section 2 page 18).